2009 Distinguished Instructor Short Course
Distinguished Instructor Series, No. 12

sponsored by the

Society of Exploration Geophysicists

European Association of Geoscientists & Engineers

Petroleum Geoengineering:
Integration of Static and Dynamic Models

presented by

Patrick Corbett

Society of Exploration Geophysicists
The international society of applied geophysics

EUROPEAN
ASSOCIATION OF
GEOSCIENTISTS &
ENGINEERS

ISBN 978-1-56080-086-6 (Series)
ISBN 978-1-56080-153-5 (Volume)

© 2009
Society of Exploration Geophysicists
P. O. Box 702740
Tulsa, OK USA 74170-2740

Printed in the U.S.A.

Library of Congress Cataloging-in-Publication Data

Distinguished Instructor Short Course (2009 : Tulsa, Okla.)

  Petroleum geoengineering : integration of static and dynamic models : 2009 Distinguished Instructor Short Course / presented by Patrick Corbett ; sponsored by the Society of Exploration Geophysicists [and] European Association of Geoscientists & Engineers.

    p. cm. -- (Distinguished instructor series ; no. 12)

  Includes bibliographical references and index.

  ISBN 978-1-56080-153-5 (volume : alk. paper) -- ISBN 978-1-56080-086-6 (series : alk. paper)

  1. Petroleum engineering--Congresses. 2. Petroleum--Geology--Mathematical models--Congresses. 3. Petroleum--Geology--Statistical methods--Congresses. 4. Petroleum reserves--Congresses. I. Society of Exploration Geophysicists. II. European Association of Geoscientists and Engineers. III. Title.

  TN870.53.D57 2009

  622'.3382--dc22

                              2009001209

Inspiration

"If we aspire to comprehend the origins of an oil field, we need to have the geologist, the chemist, and the physicist working together, learning from each other."
— Ivan M. Gubkin, 1871–1939

"The best way to identify and quantify rock framework and pore space variations is through the deliberate and integrated use of engineering and earth-science technology."
— Harris and Hewitt, 1977

Inspiration

Dedication

To Hugo, Jessica, William, and Kate

SEG and EAGE

*wish to thank the following
for their generous contributions*

About the Author

Patrick W. M. Corbett has been at the Institute of Petroleum Engineering at Heriot-Watt University in Edinburgh, Scotland, since 1993. He recently completed a five-year stint as head of the institute and is now the Total Professor of Petroleum Geoengineering. He has researched and published widely in petroleum geology, geophysics, petrophysics, and reservoir engineering. Corbett worked as exploration geologist and development geologist for Unocal from 1979 through 1989 in the United Kingdom, the Netherlands, and Indonesia. He acted as exploration manager in his last role in industry before turning to an academic career.

Corbett earned a B.Sc. in geology from Exeter University, Devon, U. K., in 1977; an M.Sc. in micropalaeontology from University College, London, U. K., in 1978; a postgraduate diploma from Kingston University, London, in 1982; and a Ph.D. in petroleum engineering in 1993 and D.Sc. in petroleum geoengineering in 2006, both from Heriot-Watt University. He is a member of EAGE, SEG, AAPG, SPWLA, SCA, and SPE and is a chartered geologist (Geological Society) and a chartered scientist (Science Council). Corbett was a Distinguished Lecturer for SPE on integration of geology and well testing in 1998–1999 and for EAGE on petroleum geoengineering in 1998. He received the 2005 Wegener Medal from EAGE for integration of geoscience and geoengineering and the 2006 SPE Europe and Russia Regional Technical Award for distinguished contribution to petroleum engineering in the area of reservoir description and dynamics.

Society of Exploration Geophysicists
The international society of applied geophysics

EUROPEAN
ASSOCIATION OF
GEOSCIENTISTS &
ENGINEERS

Dear DISC Participant:

It is a great pleasure to welcome you to the twelfth annual SEG/EAGE Distinguished Instructor Short Course (DISC), "Petroleum Geoengineering: Integration of Static and Dynamic Models," by Patrick Corbett. SEG, EAGE, and your local society are proud to provide this premier course in subsurface education.

With rapidly changing technologies, geoscientists around the world have an increasing need to acquire expert technical knowledge. SEG's Professional Development program — the SEG/EAGE DISC, the SEG Distinguished Lecturer, the SEG/AAPG Distinguished Lecturer, the SEG Honorary Lecturers, and Online DL Library — aids in the promotion of technologies that will have a significant impact on geophysics and geoscience. Likewise, EAGE supports Geoscience Education through EAGE Education Tours and EAGE Education Days events, the joint SEG/EAGE DISC, EAGE Distinguished Lecturer and short-course programs, and free member access to geoscience e-learning modules.

Recent previous DISC programs were:

- "Petroleum Systems of Deepwater Settings," by Paul Weimer, in 2004
- "Insights and Methods for 4D Reservoir Monitoring and Characterization," by Rodney Calvert, in 2005
- "Seismic Attribute Mapping of Structure and Stratigraphy," by Kurt Marfurt, in 2006
- "Concepts and Applications in 3D Seismic Imaging," by Biondo Biondi, in 2007
- "Reservoir Geophysics: Applications," by William Abriel, in 2008

Education in geophysics and geoscience is one of the top priorities for SEG and EAGE. The DISC program affords important opportunities for local geophysical organizations to provide first-rate geophysical education at modest cost. The program is truly a cooperative effort of many people in our societies dedicated to the promotion and advancement of geophysics. Your participation is key to its continued success.

We are honored to have Patrick Corbett as instructor for our 2009 DISC program. This is a great opportunity to learn from one of our profession's recognized experts in the multidiscipline linkage of geologic, geophysical, petrophysical, and reservoir-engineering techniques used at various scales to describe and model petroleum reservoirs. We encourage you to take advantage of this opportunity to broaden your perspectives through participation in the 2009 DISC.

Sincerely,

Larry Lines
SEG President

Phil Christie
EAGE President

Acknowledgments

The author would like to take this opportunity to thank his many colleagues and students for their support and stimulation over the years, particularly Jerry Jensen, Phil Ringrose, Ken Sorbie, Jon Lewis, Sandy Tudhope, John Underhill, Gillian Pickup, Tim Good, Shiyi Zheng, Moe Pinisetti, Andy Gardiner, David Potter, Olivier Dubrule, Dave Bowen, Andy Hurst, Peter Frykman, Gary Couples, Helen Lewis, Leon Barens, Septi Anggraeni, Olivier Kirstetter, Khalifa Mohammed, Yasin Ellabed, Jorge Gomes, Mike Christie, David Davies, Colin MacBeth, and Jean-Marie Questiaux. The author has spent many hours discussing and developing geoengineering ideas with these geoscientists and engineers and others (with apologies) who are not mentioned. Phil Ringrose kindly provided a review, and Jeff Johnson provided some useful comments.

Second, the author wishes to thank Total for supporting his academic position at Heriot-Watt University for more than 15 years, thereby allowing time and space for the ideas in this volume to be developed.

Finally, the author would like to thank his employer, Heriot-Watt University, for allowing him the sabbatical time to undertake this SEG/EAGE DISC tour and SEG and EAGE for sponsoring this volume and the DISC tour. He also thanks Anne H. Thomas, copy editor, and Rowena Mills, Jennifer Cobb, and Ted Bakamjian of the SEG publications department for editing and producing the volume so professionally. The author also appreciates the assistance of Peter Pangman, Tom Agnew, and Cecilia Martin of the SEG professional development department and Anne-Claire Hoensen, EAGE education manager.

— Patrick Corbett
January 2009

Table of Contents

Chapter 1   Author's Perspective and Geoengineering Context

The author has more than 30 years of experience in addressing the aspects of the petroleum industry that continue to challenge that industry — the effective measurement, interpretation, and modeling of subsurface reservoirs for efficient petroleum reservoir development. After a 10-year industry career with Unocal, the author joined the academic institution at which he has spent the past 20 years teaching aspects of development geoscience. With that experience, he has developed a personal vision for integration — a vision gained from practical field experience and more than 50 publications and informed by a formal education across a range of geoscience and engineering subjects, including basic geology, micropaleontology, geostatistics, petroleum engineering, and geoengineering.

The range of topics with which the author has experience includes aspects of geology, petrophysics, geophysics, geostatistics, and reservoir engineering. Efficient and effective integration of those topics is considered to be a subject worthy of human endeavor in its own right. Such integration has been termed *geoengineering*, or making practical use of the subsurface (Corbett, 1997). The present SEG/EAGE Distinguished Instructor Short Course draws from published and unpublished work and aims to further the integrated concepts that have been defined in the earlier literature.

Increasing public interest in oil-production forecasts and particularly in "peak-oil" forecasts (Figure 1) will encourage industrywide development of closer integration and investment in improved oil recovery. That effort will help the industry meet projections of growing demand for petroleum liquids (Figure 2).

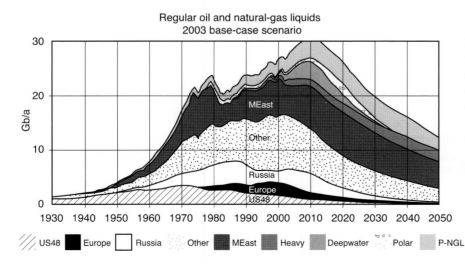

Figure 1. Estimation of oil production, showing the concept of approaching "peak oil." Gb/a = gigabarrels (billion barrels) per year. From ASPO (2002), accessed 2002. Used by permission.

It is suggested that traditional reservoir and/or petroleum engineers focus primarily on the specifics of a single field or small group of fields — i.e., on traditional reservoir engineering for field-development planning. It also is believed that petroleum geoengineers can step back and consider their global success with respect to oil recovery. A global perspective allows geoscientists to extend the comparison of recovery factors by geologic environment (e.g., Figure 3, from the U. S. Gulf Coast, and Figure 4, from the North Sea). Understanding the controlling aspects of these geologic-environment recovery factors will help workers to improve global recovery factors. Indeed, this one-day course seeks to inspire the latter statement of intent by the subsurface petrotechnical community.

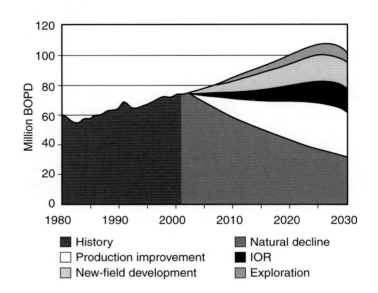

Figure 2. Projection of increasing demand for petroleum and the technologies that will be employed to delay peak oil. From Meling (2004), ©World Petroleum Council. Used by permission.

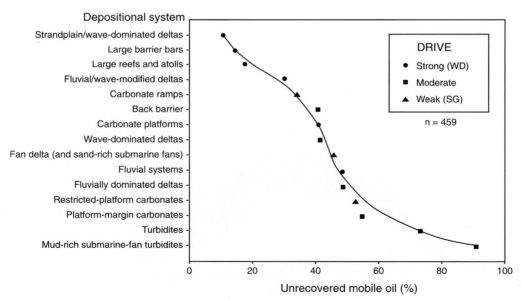

Figure 3. Recovery factors for a range of geologic environments, based on U. S. Gulf Coast data. WD = water drive; SG = solution gas drive. From Tyler and Finley (1991). Used by permission.

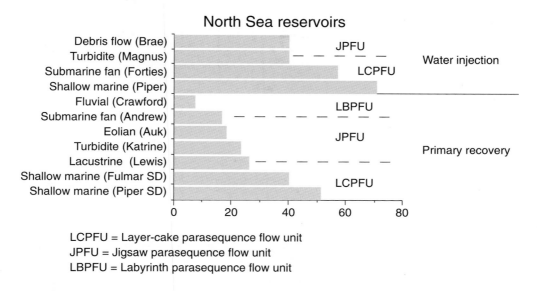

LCPFU = Layer-cake parasequence flow unit
JPFU = Jigsaw parasequence flow unit
LBPFU = Labyrinth parasequence flow unit

Figure 4. Recovery factors for a range of geologic scenarios, based on North Sea data.

Petroleum geoengineering has arisen from foundations provided by development of the quantitative reservoir description that was promoted by reservoir characterization in the 1980s (Lake, 1989) and by integrated reservoir evaluation in the 1990s (Cosentino, 2001). Cosentino (2001) noted that no project can be integrated fully and that each improvement only can make the product less disintegrated than it was previously. Thus, petroleum geoengineering seeks to promote ever-increasing integration of the disciplines while recognizing that perhaps the ultimate utopia of full integration is unachievable.

Prior to 1980, when the author began to work in the oil patch, workflows were effectively sequential (Figure 5). The 1990s saw a greater convergence and interaction among the disciplines of reservoir engineering, production geology, and production seismic work (Figure 6).

The vision for petroleum geoengineering is of an all-encompassing discipline (Figure 7) that contains the functions and skill sets of geologists, engineers, petrophysicists, and geophysicists. An individual petroleum geoengineer will have a "center of gravity" within this discipline space, stemming from his educational background (usually his first college degree). Petroleum geoengineering grows logically from the evolution of the reservoir-development workflows in our industry. It is driven by the need to improve recovery, and it is enabled by creation of appropriate software platforms.

As a new, all-encompassing discipline, petroleum geoengineering needs an agreed-on framework (the basis of any course syllabus) with which to cover the relevant aspects of geology, geophysics, petrophysics, geostatistics, and reservoir and petroleum engineering. Corbett (1997) identified five subject areas that might form the core of petroleum geoengineering: architecture; properties; modeling, including the traditional geoscience and petrophysical aspects; simulation using engineering; and management. These subjects form a logical sequence with feedback loops (Figure 8).

Figure 5. Pre-1980 sequential workflow for reservoir development. Courtesy of Don Best. Used by permission.

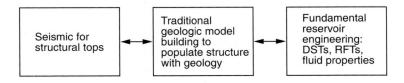

Figure 6. In the early 1990s, a more integrated workflow for reservoir development emerged. Courtesy of Don Best. Used by permission.

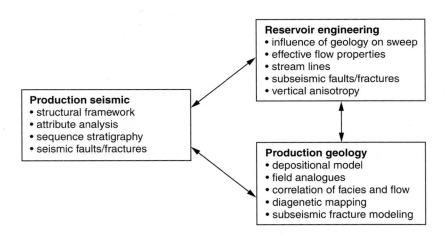

Figure 7. A 2010 or even 2020 vision shows geoengineering as a more holistic approach that will include professionals developed from core disciplines.

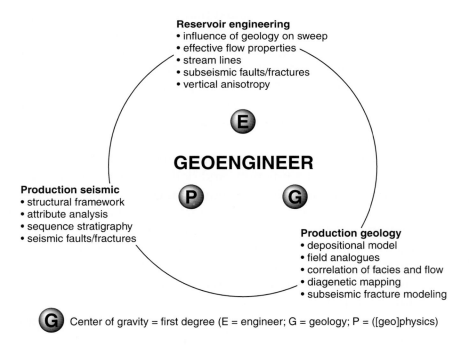

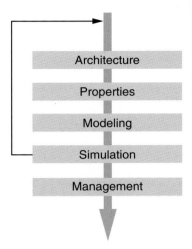

Figure 8. A simplified petroleum-geoengineering workflow has an illustrative feedback loop to guide additional data collection.

This book was prepared to accompany a one-day course and is intended to provide readers with a road map to follow in their subsurface work, whether they are geologists, geophysicists, or engineers. Readers should be able to identify herein many points of resonance with their own working environments. It is hoped that this book will stimulate in geoscientists a greater resolve to integrate disciplines within their organizations and that thereby it will stimulate an improvement in oil-recovery factors.

Chapter 2   Background to Geoengineering

It has been recognized for many years that "the best way to identify and quantify rock-framework and pore-space variations is through the deliberate and integrated use of engineering and earth-science technology" (Harris and Hewitt, 1977, p. 761, published at the start of this author's career). Fred Aminzadeh, a former Unocal colleague of the author and 2007–2008 SEG president, later called for integration "of disciplines, not results" and used the term *geoengineer* in the sense of being a possible "torchbearer" (Aminzadeh, 1996).

The industry's management teams in the 1990s shared several concerns. There were general moves toward open-plan offices; it was felt that the absence of walls would encourage integration. Management always had struggled to measure and reward integration effectively. There were reports of one company poaching high-performing teams from another when the market arose for integrated teams. Finally, many people were concerned that the provision of greater breadth conflicted with the development of greater depth. Indeed, perhaps the development of breadth — the petroleum-geoengineering model — conflicts with preservation of deep expertise and remains a major challenge for the industry today. This concern certainly can foster a resistance that needs to be overcome if geoengineering is to become adopted more widely. Geoengineering in itself might one day come to be considered an expertise.

Individuals also have had concerns. The 1990s were a period of sustained low oil prices. An individual had to weigh development of team skills against development of greater depth while keeping job security in mind. The absence of appropriate financial or promotional incentives to become technically more broad-based rather than more specialized also would have discouraged any change in behavior.

Society too has concerns. The price of oil depends largely on available supplies. With increasing demand and falling reserves — two drivers associated with a high degree of uncertainty — the price of oil is set to rise in the long term. Thus, our disciplines have a social responsibility to maximize reserves and to develop scientific understanding of the subsurface so that the sustainability agenda can be engaged further.

Chapter 3   Definition of *Geoengineering*

Until a few years ago, no formal definition of *petroleum geoengineering* existed (Corbett, 2006), nor does the term *geoengineering* itself appear to have a formal definition, although it has reasonably wide usage. Indeed, inserting "define:geoengineering" into a search engine on the Web fails to produce a definition, in contrast to "define:engineering," which produces many diverse definitions, as might be expected.

A search of the Internet in the late 1990s revealed several civil-engineering geoengineering projects that involve fluids and subsurface exploitation — including salt-cavern excavation and hazardous-waste disposal. There also were calls at that time for chartered-geoengineer (CGeoEng) status for those working at the geotechnical interface of mining engineering and geology (Rhoden, 1997). A geoengineer is in that respect a natural outgrowth of the engineering geologist or geologic engineer (Fookes, 1998).

An April 2004 Web search on geoengineering produced nearly 18,000 hits; a search in May 2008 produced 222,000 hits. Clearly, the term is in increasingly common usage. The expression is used in a variety of contexts, as we see in examples from the 2004 survey:

- The Department of Civil and Environmental Engineering at the University of California, Berkeley, offers a program in geoengineering (http://www.ce.berkeley. edu/geo/index.php) that replaces the traditional geotechnical program because of expansion in scope and coverage. This program covers petroleum engineering, rock mechanics, and reservoir engineering.

- "Geoengineering is the intentional large-scale manipulation of the global environment," states D. W. Keith in an article in the *Encyclopedia of Global Change* (Keith, 2002, p. 420), in which he also identifies a paper by C. Marchetti, "On geoengineering and the CO_2 problem," as being the first published occurrence of the term *geoengineering* (Marchetti, 1977). Keith goes on to say that sequestration (capture and storage) of CO_2 is classified rightly as a novel geoengineering endeavor — rather than as conventional pollution mitigation — because it fails to compensate for emissions after they occur on a global scale (Keith, 2001). Keith emphasizes that scale and intent are central to the common meaning of *geoengineering*. In Keith's sense, *scale* means at the largest planetary scale.

- Stanford University has several geoengineering research projects in its Global Climate and Energy Project (http://gcep.stanford.edu/research/geoengineering.html). Those projects (large-scale CO_2 removal from the atmosphere; building a giant reflector between the earth and sun; placing a layer of reflective chemicals in the upper atmosphere) inevitably would alter the climate on a global scale.

- Geoengineering is the name of a Czech company that specializes in a range of geotechnical activities, including mining and tunneling (http://www.geoengineering.cz).

- The GeoEngineering Centre at Queen's University/Royal Military College in Kingston, Ontario, Canada, was founded in 2001 and is dedicated to innovation and advancement of knowledge in geotechnical, geohydrologic, geochemical, geomechanical, and geosynthetics engineering (http://www.geoeng.ca/).

- The School of Civil Engineering at the Asian Institute of Technology, based in Pathumthani, Thailand, has a program in petroleum geoengineering that deals with issues in the upstream sector of the industry. The program emphasizes the importance of courses in information and computer science for modern geoengineers (http://www.sce.ait.ac.th/).

- The International Tunnelling and Underground Space Association (ITA) posts on its Web site a position paper titled "Geoengineering considerations in the optimum use of underground space" (http://www.ita-aites.org/cms/).

From the review in hand, one can see that *geoengineering* appears in a variety of contexts that includes references to making practical use of the subsurface or making optimum use of underground space; references to intentional large-scale manipulation of the global environment; and integrated training for the mining, geotechnical, and/or petroleum industries.

The term *geoengineer* entered the petroleum public's consciousness through the literature in the early 1990s. Developments in the field until that time had included training in geoengineering at UNICAMP, Sao Paulo, Brazil, and at the GeoEngineering Group at Los Alamos National Laboratory in New Mexico. In 1996, Fred Aminzadeh also called for the integration of disciplines into what he called "geo-engineering." L. Cosentino (2001) published the first textbook that focused on integrated reservoir studies, but it looked primarily at improvements to current processes rather than addressing emerging disciplines.

A recent Internet search (May 2008) on petroleum geoengineering produced 21,000 hits, many of which identified major efforts at CSIRO in Australia and at the Asian Institute of Technology, Thailand. In addition, a new professor of petroleum geoengineering, Quentin Fisher, has been named at the University of Leeds (www.see.leeds.ac.uk/people/q.fisher).

Petroleum geoengineering has been defined as the "intentional manipulation of the subsurface environment, as practiced by the petroleum industry, with global impact" (Corbett, 2006, p. 4). That practice relies heavily on the use of computer models that require effective measurement, interpretation, and modeling of subsurface reservoirs for efficient petroleum reservoir development. Incidentally, CO_2 storage in petroleum reservoirs or nearby saline aquifers would fall naturally under the heading of petroleum geoengineering and would require the integrated approach proposed in this course.

Although the term *geoengineering* is used widely and is claimed by various earth engineers for their exclusive use, the word obviously is already in broad usage. Common to all its applications are systematic measurement, interpretation, and modeling of media for engineering studies, using a complete, interdisciplinary approach. In the petroleum context, this becomes systematic measurement, interpretation, and modeling of geologic media in the subsurface for optimum exploitation of petroleum reservoirs. Such an effort requires knowledge drawn from the disciplines of geostatistics, geology, geophysics, petrophysics, geomechanics, and reservoir engineering.

Rock mechanics, a discipline that spans a range from mining to petroleum engineering, is worthy of special mention. The term *geoengineering* often is applied to geotechnical activities based inherently on rock mechanics, so rock mechanics (measurements in the laboratory and field and simulation modeling for prediction) also can be categorized as geoengineering. This is consistent with attempts to promote a chartered-geoengineer certification by some people in the mining industry (Rhoden, 1997), thereby recognizing the fact that work in the subsurface environment of mining needs practitioners with formal backgrounds in geoscience and engineering. A rock-mechanics professional in the petroleum industry should identify closely with the approach promoted for petroleum geoengineering.

Many engineering decisions in oil-field development are based on computer models of the subsurface. In their representation of geologic media, geostatisticians and reservoir engineers put specific requirements on the properties of cells in those models. Thus, geologists and petrophysicists (along with rock mechanicists and rock physicists) are required to source the appropriate data for that purpose. The specific shared end goal defines a common petroleum-geoengineering agenda across the various contributory disciplines.

Petroleum geoengineering and its practitioners, petroleum geoengineers, are concerned with global aspects of petroleum engineering in the broadest context — with workflow processes that are transportable and generic — rather than with the specific challenge of engineering a specific field. That is why a geoengineer is concerned with simplified architectural matrices, recovery factors, sampling strategies, the genetic origin of petrophysical properties (genetic petrophysics), and petrophysical and well-testing catalogs, all of which are discussed in this book. In that sense, by seeking to improve recovery factors on the global scale, petroleum geoengineering is consistent with the global objectives used by Keith (2001) for geoengineering.

The author's aspiration for petroleum geoengineering to address global challenges facing society — thereby exploiting the double meaning of *geo* that is found in *geology* and *geopolitics* — might be asking too much. Clearly, however, no inconsistencies exist between the definition of *petroleum geoengineering* presented by Corbett (2006) and previous widespread usage of the term *geoengineering* (which has been applied very broadly and which lacks a specific definition). Petroleum geoengineers will make a significant contribution to the major global energy-resource budget for many years to come.

Chapter 4   The Geoengineering Challenge

What is it about geologic media that makes them so challenging to engineers? Engineering models of the subsurface usually are based on estimation of some effective property, whether the models are analytic or are cellular based (in the latter case, the properties are thought to be effective at the scale of a single cell). Therefore, a systematic approach to measuring, interpreting, and modeling the subsurface needs to consider the scale at which the measurement has been made, the interpretation model used to analyze the data, and the modeling technique used to simulate the data. The response to any engineering process in the subsurface will be predicted most effectively by an analytic model or a simulation model.

Geologic media are essentially hierarchical, with multiple-length scales reflecting the depositional process (it is assumed in this book that most reservoirs are in sedimentary rocks, but those concepts can be extended to metamorphic and igneous rocks). All measurements taken in a rock will have to consider the scale of measurement relative to the geologic-length scale, the method used to interpret the measurements, and the scales that must be incorporated into the effective media.

This book is concerned primarily with permeability because it relates directly to oil recovery. Effective permeability is defined as the single equivalent property of a homogeneous volume upscaled from all the heterogeneous point measurements at smaller volume scales. Measurement and scaling of effective permeability are major challenges in petroleum-development projects.

The effective-medium concept was proposed by Bear and Bachmat (1990) as the fundamental property that governs flow in a porous medium (Figure 1). In a porous medium, a volume threshold exists above which the effective property (either porosity or permeability) can be defined. The effective-flow equations — such as Darcy's law — hold only for those larger volumes in which small changes in volume do not lead to large changes in measured properties. Identification of representative elementary volumes is critical in measuring and modeling properties such as permeability. We will see later that a rock can have many representative volumes at various scales, and that characteristic provides a fundamental challenge to the geoengineer. In the following sections, we consider the basic reservoir-engineering measurements and their scales relative to geologic media.

Porosity

Porosity, often represented by ϕ, is the ratio of pore volume to bulk volume. In sandstones, it usually ranges from a few percent to more than 30%. This is a range of one order of magnitude. Porosity in a typical sandstone is controlled by packing, grain

Figure 1. The fundamentals of flow in porous media are defined here by the effective-medium theory. See text for further explanation. Adapted from *Introduction to Modeling of Transport Phenomena in Porous Media*, 1990, p. 25, by J. Bear and Y. Bachmat, Figure 1.2.3, copyright Kluwer Academic Publishers. With kind permission of Springer Science and Business Media.

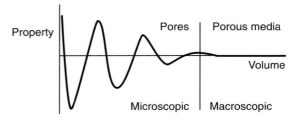

shape, grain sorting, and cements. In the petroleum industry, porosity can be measured at several scales:

- submillimeter scale in thin sections, by point counting
- centimeter scale in core plugs, by gas expansion
- decimeter scale in subsurface wireline logs, with knowledge of matrix properties
- decameter scale, by inversion of seismic impedances

Modeling from one scale to another is relatively simple because porosity is an additive property, which allows averaging techniques to be used effectively. Because the range of porosities within a reservoir is relatively small and the central limit theorem implies that many samples will approach a normal distribution, porosity prediction is easier than permeability prediction, in which permeability often has a skewed distribution. Carbonates can have more extreme variations in porosity, resulting in increased prediction challenges. Porosity has a major impact on volumes of hydrocarbons in place, but it controls flow and recovery only indirectly.

Permeability

Permeability, often represented by k, is a constant (in units of area) that relates flow rate to pressure drop over a length scale. Permeability varies according to the same controlling properties of sediments as does porosity, but critically, permeability is also very sensitive to grain size, clay morphology, and fractures. Permeability commonly varies by several orders of magnitude in a reservoir and usually has a nonnormal (non-Gaussian) distribution. In addition, it is a nonadditive property that is very dependent on the experimental setup (e.g., linear flow in a plug, radial flow in a well test, and vertical or horizontal permeability, to illustrate a few challenges). Determination of the effective permeability by using averaging depends greatly on the type and direction of flow. Permeability is interpreted from experiments at various scales:

- millimeter-scale hemispheric flow, measured by a probe permeameter (Figure 2a)
- centimeter-scale linear flow, in a core plug (Figure 2b)
- meter-scale vertical flow, in a vertical pressure profile
- decameter-scale, exemplified by radial flow in a drillstem test

Scaling rules and techniques must be developed for comparing those measurements across the geologic-length scales. Probe-permeameter, plug, and whole-core measurements allow comparisons at different scales. Permeability has a direct impact on recovery rates and recovery factors.

Porosity and permeability relationships

Porosity and permeability are related to the textural properties of sandstone (Brayshaw et al., 1996). Our industry tends to refer to "poroperms" as if porosity and permeability were a single property. Relationships between the two can be extremely complex (Figure 3), however, and understanding the relationships is critical to geoengineering predictions. A standard reservoir workflow might measure both porosity and permeability but would model only porosity and then predict permeability from a porosity-permeability relationship. Some studies (Figure 4) show more complex relationships.

Lorenz plot and modified Lorenz plot

Because porosity and permeability vary in reservoirs, other plots have been developed at the same (core-plug) scale to capture the variability of the two properties. The Lorenz plot is an ordered crossplot (essentially from high permeability to low permeability) of cumulative permeability (called transmissivity) versus cumulative porosity (storativity) (Pinisetti, 1999; Jensen et al., 2000).

On a Lorenz plot (Figure 5), departure of the curve from the 45° line is a measure of heterogeneity. In a modified Lorenz plot, the plugs are ordered stratigraphically (referred to as a "stratigraphically modified Lorenz plot" by Gunter et al., 1997). Such a plot

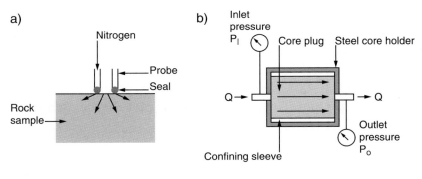

Figure 2. Comparison of the flow regimes for two permeability-measuring devices: (a) hemispheric flow in the probe permeameter and (b) linear flow in the core-plug cell. In each case, Darcy's law assumes an effective (i.e., uniform) medium to interpret the permeability value for the experiment.

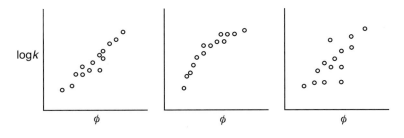

Figure 3. Schematic showing simple relationships between porosity (ϕ) and the logarithm of permeability ($\log k$). Some of those data sets might be approximated by a single empirical relationship, whereas others will require a different approach.

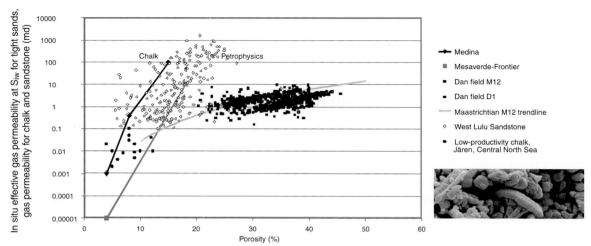

Figure 4. Extreme variation in porosity and permeability from a combined clastic and carbonate data set of rocks from Denmark. Modified from Frykman (2002); courtesy of P. Frykman. Used by permission.

Figure 5. (a) Lorenz plot and (b) modified Lorenz plot used to represent heterogeneity and location of zones of high transmissivity.

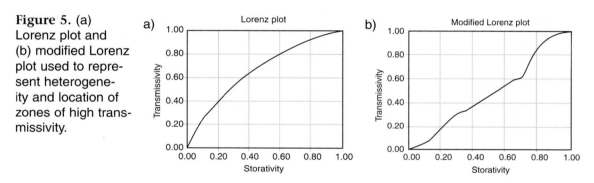

enables identification of "speed zones" where high transmissivity suggests that inflow can be expected to be higher than it is over other intervals. The modified Lorenz plot provides an excellent tool for linking the static description of a reservoir (e.g., a series of core plugs) to a dynamic one (a flow profile). The modified Lorenz plot can be used as a model for production profile logs.

Capillary pressure

Rock typing is an approach to classifying porosity and permeability clusters (core samples) by identifying similar pore-throat and size relationships. Rock typing therefore is a petrophysical classification of reservoir rocks and is a fundamental link between static sedimentologic description and dynamic fluid flow.

A mercury-injection capillary-pressure curve commonly is used to investigate pore-size distributions and is a good discriminator of textural contrasts in clastics (Figure 6). The distribution of capillary curves in a reservoir controls the distribution of hydrocarbons in place.

Selecting an effective capillary-pressure curve in a reservoir with many rock types is a geoengineering challenge because it depends on the distribution of rock types relative to the oil-water contact (Figure 7).

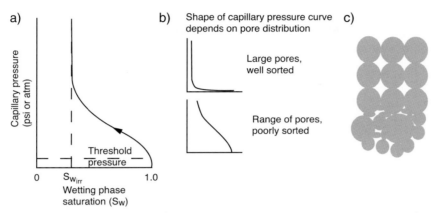

Figure 6. (a) Typical capillary-pressure curve showing the variation of wetting-phase (usually water) saturation with increasing differential pressure between the two phases (oil and water) that occurs with increasing height of the hydrocarbon column. (b) and (c) The shape of the capillary-pressure curve is controlled by textural properties of the sediment (e.g., by grain size and sorting).

Petrotyping

The traditional rock-typing approach is to start with a set of samples from a well and then split them by using declustering techniques. An alternative approach is to map the data onto a predetermined base map of classes in porosity-permeability space. The latter approach is called *petrotyping* (Corbett and Potter, 2004).

One traditional method used to identify rock types is the use of hydraulic units. Hydraulic units (Amaefule et al., 1993) are recognized by their flow-zone indicator (FZI), which is determined from clusters of porosity and permeability data from core-plug measurements, as follows,

$$\text{FZI} = \frac{\text{RQI}}{\Phi_z} = \frac{0.0314\sqrt{\dfrac{k}{\phi}}}{\left(\dfrac{\phi}{1-\phi}\right)},$$ (1)

where RQI is reservoir quality index.

For a given porosity, the permeability can be calculated by a rearrangement of equation 1, as follows:

$$K = \phi\left(\frac{(\text{FZI})x\left(\dfrac{\phi}{1-\phi}\right)}{0.0314}\right)^2 \dots$$ (2)

FZI is determined uniquely for a rock type when porosity is 50%. However, by selecting a systematic range of FZI values (Table 1) and substituting in equation 2 for all values of porosity above 5%, a series of global-hydraulic-element (GHE) boundaries can be determined (plotted in Figure 8).

Figure 7. (left) Three capillary-pressure curves controlling the distribution of saturation in (right) the reservoir as a function of rock-property variations.

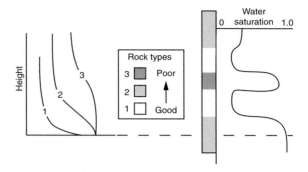

Table 1. Hydraulic-unit lower boundaries (shown as FZI values) for 10 global hydraulic elements (GHEs).

FZI	GHE	FZI	GHE
48	10	1.5	5
24	9	0.75	4
12	8	0.375	3
6	7	0.1875	2
3	6	0.0938	1

Figure 8. Varying petrophysical petrotype classes, predefined by systematic FZI values. (a) The core-plug data set overlain on the resulting petrotype base map of a shallow-marine clastic reservoir shows that multiple hydraulic elements are present. (b) In contrast, a chalk reservoir shows a single global hydraulic element (GHE). The differences between these two chosen cases are deliberately extreme. However, the approach shows how a combined plug data set (Figure 4) might be broken down into component petrophysical rock types (not to be confused with lithologic types).

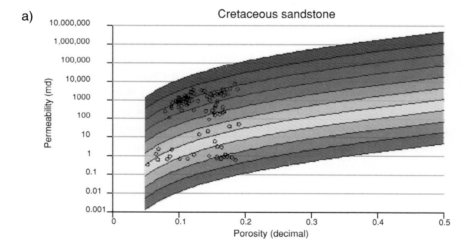

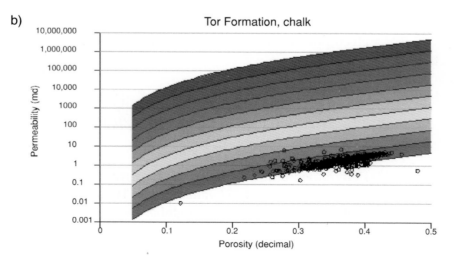

Because the rock types in the petrotyping approach are global in the sense that they are predetermined, the base map (Figure 8) can be used to determine quickly whether a reservoir has single or multiple rock types. Different reservoirs also can be compared systematically. The poroperm base map provides a rapid technique for screening and selecting core data for further petrographic and special core analysis.

Global hydraulic units have been shown to have different textural properties (Svrisky et al., 2004) and different capillary pressures (Mohammed and Corbett, 2003). The GHE approach helps workers to identify the appropriate scale of porosity and permeability heterogeneity they will need to capture in a reservoir model. Ideally, the smallest-scale reservoir model will have elements (grid blocks) containing a single GHE. The GHE is the petrophysically appropriate scale at which to distribute poroperms because porosity and permeability are constrained to a relatively small range by definition of the elements. Elements identified in a systematic way can be identified in various wells (on the basis of core data extrapolated to logs) and then correlated and mapped.

Wettability

Wettability is a pore-scale phenomenon that usually is expressed as the contact angle between the water-oil interface and the mineral surface. It controls the relationship between fluids and mineral surfaces (Figure 9) in a pore. Wettability is critical to the understanding of a displacement mechanism (by gas or water) in an oil field. The distribution of wettability in a reservoir is complex — it can vary within a single pore (mixed wettability) or among layers or regions (fractional wettability), and those definitions imply scale dependency.

It is possible to image variations in wettability at the pore scale (Figure 9), but any laboratory experimental technique relies on measurements at the core-plug scale. In this sense, wettability measurements on rocks are larger-scale effective properties for experimental conditions. Conditioning the samples to reservoir conditions (i.e., restoring to the original wettability state) with no drilling-fluid contamination is an additional challenge when making wettability measurements.

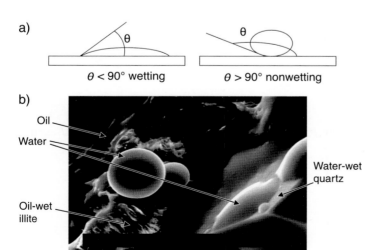

a)

$\theta < 90°$ wetting $\theta > 90°$ nonwetting

b)

Oil
Water
Water-wet quartz
Oil-wet illite

Figure 9. Wettability (a) defined schematically for ideal mineral surfaces and (b) illustrated in a single pore. In the image of a pore, the water on the left is repelled by kaolinite, but on the right, it is attracted to the quartz surface. Environmental scanning electron-microscope image courtesy of Jim Buckman. Used by permission.

Relative permeability

Relative permeability describes the way in which fluids (here we consider two phases, oil and water) move through the rock as saturations of the phases change. In this consideration, relative permeability is a pore-scale phenomenon. Relative permeability is an important simulation parameter because it determines the water-breakthough profile and the production performance after water breaks through to producing wells.

Relative permeability is controlled by the wettability (Figure 10) and requires (1) careful measurement at the core-plug scale and (2) upscaling to account for numerical grid-block size and geologic heterogeneity. Relative permeability at the large simulation scale ideally should be described for each rock type (Mohammed and Corbett, 2003) and for each region (to take into account fault-block and/or crest-to-flank variations).

Acoustic properties

Acoustic properties usually are measured at the core-plug scale, following well-established procedures in rock physics. Velocities are measured at varying confining pressures (Figure 11). Hysteresis effects vary for different samples as a function of lithology.

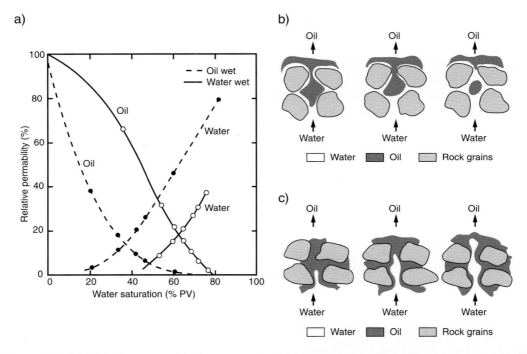

Figure 10. (a) Relative permeability curves for (b) water-wet and (c) oil-wet systems. % PV = percent pore volume.

Many of the challenges that geoengineers face as they measure effective permeability are shared by geophysicists because geophysical measurements also rely heavily on effective-medium theory and require some sort of upscaling. An additional issue in rock physics is that measurements taken at high frequency (which is typical in the laboratory) must be converted for use at low frequency (in the field). Where rock physics has been done in a rock-typing framework (as in Figure 12), it is possible to see advantages to classifying rock-physics variations by rock type. Use of petrophysical rock types to populate a reservoir model with flow properties allows the model to be populated with rock-physics properties at the same time.

Well testing

Well testing provides the opportunity to measure permeability at scales larger than core or wireline-log scales and under in situ conditions. In situ considerations differ from many laboratory setups because (1) the overburden causes significant pressure differences and (2) flow tests usually are conducted at end-point relative-permeability conditions. Any comparison between laboratory and field measurements of properties must take these differences into account.

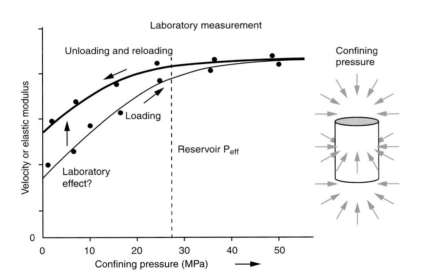

Figure 11. Laboratory measurement of acoustic properties. To cover the range of acoustic properties, sample selection in a reservoir should be related to the samples selected for rock typing and other petrophysical measurements so that models can be generated for flow and acoustic responses. After MacBeth (2007). Used by permission.

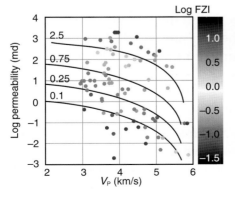

Figure 12. Compressional velocity and permeability variations for different rock types. From Prasad (2002). Used by permission.

Figure 13. A simple flow and shut-in sequence during a well test. Here, *p* denotes elapsed time, and *q* denotes flow rate. Courtesy of Shiyi Zheng. Used by permission.

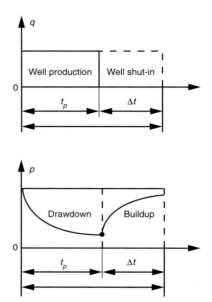

Well tests (i.e., drillstem tests, production tests) are designed to measure flow rate and pressure drop during a flowing period and a subsequent shut-in period (Figure 13). Both those periods can be interpreted, but often the buildup period is selected because at that time, advantages can result from the rate being effectively zero. This condition makes it easier to interpret the pressure response. To calculate permeability, a flow model has to be fitted. The simplest model is an infinite-acting radial flow model, in which pressure will continue to rise as a linear function of the logarithm of time, in the absence of any different boundary condition. Under those conditions, the rate of change of pressure build-up remains constant to the logarithm of time (Figure 14).

A plot of the rate of change of pressure versus the logarithm of time will show a plateau region (Figure 14). Interpretation of the plateau and knowledge of the thickness of the reservoir will give permeability. Such variations can have significant importance geologically and can indicate the following:

- near-wellbore phenomena, such as fractures, high-permeability streaks, and cemented nodules

- geologic features away from the wellbore, such as thickening, faulting, or layering

Importance of scale in geologic systems

Geologic systems are very complex, with multiple-length scales and multiple scales of homogenization (Figure 15) (Corbett, 2006). Many workers in reservoir characterization similarly have considered extending Bear and Bachmat's idea (Bear and Bachmat, 1990) to hierarchical geologic systems (examples can be found in Nordahl [2004]). All the measurements discussed in the previous sections theoretically should take into account those length scales, although they often are ignored in practice. The properties then must be upscaled for use at different length scales.

Summarizing the challenge

Most laboratory measurements in the oil industry require effective-medium models (in the sense of Figure 1) for the interpretation to be meaningful (e.g., to be consistent with the assumptions behind Darcy's law). This drives the industry toward using uniform, homogeneous samples whenever possible. Measurements on uniform samples should allow the geoengineer to determine the effective properties, but only for that medium at that specific homogenization scale. Unfortunately, Mother Nature has deposited reservoirs that rarely are homogeneous over the entire volume. The geoengineer therefore is required to target samples that are representative. Bear and Bachmat (1990) defined the representative elementary volume (REV) as the macroscopic volume (Figure 1) over which flow in porous media could be determined by the most widely used measure, Darcy's law.

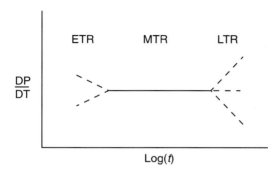

Figure 14. A definition sketch of a radial, infinite-acting plateau on a plot of the rate of change of pressure versus the logarithm of time since shut-in (for a buildup case). Near-wellbore phenomena affect the pressure response in the early time region (ETR), and phenomena away from the well affect the late time region (LTR). The middle time region (MTR) is defined by the radial flow plateau. Derivatives below the radial MTR plateau exhibit increasing permeability thickness or mobility. Derivative trends above the plateau show reduced permeability thickness or mobility. DP = pressure change; DT = time change.

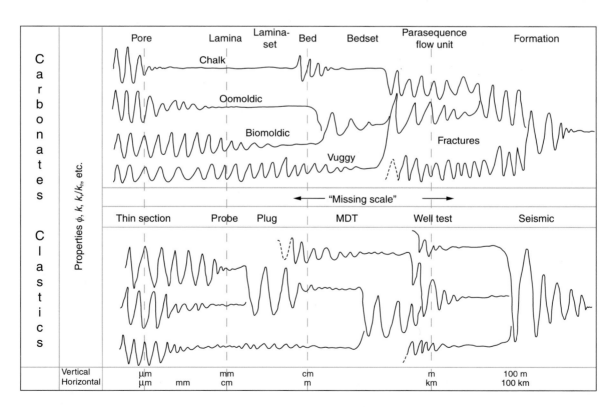

Figure 15. Hierarchical and multiple-length scales in geologic systems (Corbett, 2006), with scales of measurement superimposed. MDT = modular formation dynamics tester.

Targeting the various homogenization volumes in a reservoir requires geologic knowledge coupled with petrophysical understanding and an engineering interpretation. Tran (1996) and Caers (2005) describe some of the measurement volumes as "missing scales" to draw attention to the fact that a wide range of volumes is missing when one is considering plugs, logging tools, and well testing. Systematic measurement of rocks across all scales is the most fundamental challenge that a geoengineer faces.

Chapter 5   Core Skills of a Petroleum Geoengineer

Addressing the challenge of working with the wide range of petrophysical properties that occurs over the multiple-length scales of geologic media requires a broad background that extends across geoscience and engineering. The core skills of a petroleum geoengineer are found in the disciplines of geology, geophysics, geostatistics, petrophysics, engineering, and management. Those skills provide each of the bases that a petroleum geoengineer must visit in the course of a reservoir-description and reservoir-modeling project. Having one person with specialist-level knowledge in each of those areas brings the advantage that at an early stage, an initial model can be built to consider management options before a more detailed petrophysical characterization and/or geologic modeling is commissioned. This ensures that workers can use the available data to identify appropriate questions for modeling to address, and that ultimately leads to more useful predictions and improved recovery.

Architecture

Rocks are deposited with certain geometries that are determined by the environment of deposition, and this knowledge is fundamental to our understanding of stratigraphy. An example is found in a progradational parasequence set from a typical highstand systems tract (Figure 1). The geologic architecture is controlled by relative sea level and sediment supply. Knowledge of such systems is important for correlating reservoir flow units and detecting intrareservoir seals.

Sequence-stratigraphic concepts can be extrapolated to other environments. Models for fluvial systems can explain the stacking patterns of fluvial channels (Figure 2). As sea level rises, incised valleys are filled with a high net-to-gross (braided) fluvial system. At highstand, a meandering system might develop. In a complete fluvial sequence, one might expect a systematic vertical variation in stacking patterns, which can be exploited in modeling. Similar patterns can be found in other environments (e.g., carbonate, eolian) as a result of relative rise or fall in sea level or climate change and variations in sediment supply.

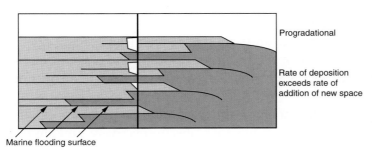

Progradational

Rate of deposition exceeds rate of addition of new space

Marine flooding surface

Figure 1. A progradational parasequence set formed by cycles of relative rise and fall in sea level under conditions of increasing sediment supply. After Van Wagoner et al., 1990, *Siliciclastic Sequence Stratigraphy in Well Logs, Cores, and Outcrops,* AAPG Methods in Exploration No. 7. AAPG©1990, reprinted by permission of the AAPG whose permission is required for further use.

Figure 2. Model for the variation in fluvial stacking patterns caused by relative fluctuations in sea level and their relationship to shallow-marine stacking; mfs = maximum flooding surface. After Shanley and McCabe, 1993, "Perspectives on the Sequence of Continental Strata," *AAPG Bulletin,* **78**, p. 544–568. AAPG©1993, reprinted by permission of the AAPG whose permission is required for further use.

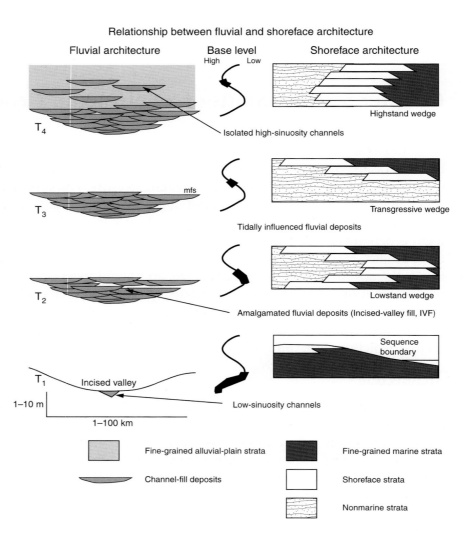

Tectonic activity can interfere with the stratigraphic patterns (Figure 3) by changing relative sea level or sediment supply during deposition or by postdepositional faulting. Faulting modifies those depositional geometries, but faults also can have systematic patterns (Figure 4).

Natural variability resulting from deposition, preservation diagenesis, and faulting tends to lead to additional reservoir complexity. However, the underlying patterns often can be recognized. A classification of reservoirs by vertical and horizontal heterogeneity forms a geologic matrix (Figure 5). Within flow units and for a given well spacing, the stacking patterns of architectural elements can be combined to produce a range of reservoir architectures. This architectural matrix is a further development of original concepts published by Weber and van Geuns (1990).

Note that the length scales — of well spacing in the horizontal plane and of flow units in the vertical — are engineering and petrophysical scales, respectively, and are not a function of geology alone. Geometries of geobodies (geologic elements), stacking patterns, and length scales are the critical issues.

Geometries of sand bodies can be measured at outcrop. For example, data on the geometry of low-angle cross-laminated sets in a shallow-marine reservoir (Figures 6 and 7) can be compared with similar data from different geographic areas and stratigraphic intervals. Such a comparison provides the geoengineer with a useful tool when a model of a shallow-marine reservoir is required.

Larger-scale stacking relationships also can be observed at outcrop. Turbidite reservoirs often comprise multiple geobodies and large-scale outcrops such as those seen in well-described sections near Ainsa in northern Spain. Modeling outcrop panels such as these helps us to understand the appearance of sedimentary heterogeneity on seismic (Figure 8) that otherwise might be confused easily with structural discontinuity.

Getting the correct architecture (stratigraphy) in a reservoir model is very critical for optimizing the recovery. Jantschik et al. (1996) published an example of a Tertiary incised valley-fill reservoir in Germany (Eich field) that shows how a revised stratigraphic model (Figure 9) incorporating new sequence-stratigraphic concepts led to improved recovery performance (Figure 10). Determining the stratigraphy in a complex field is not a simple task when there are few wells and limited seismic data.

| Vertical heterogeneity | Horizontal heterogeneity | | |
	Low	Moderate	High
Low	Wave-dominated (proximal) delta Sand-rich strand plain Barrier island	Distributary mouth bar Proximal delta front Tidal deposits Mud-rich strand plain	Meandering fluvial (single point bar) River-dominated delta (single package) Back barrier (single package)
Medium	Wave-modified (distal) delta Eolian	Shelf bars Alluvial fan Fan delta Distal delta front Wave-modified delta (proximal)	Braided river Tide-dominated delta
High	Submarine fan (Turbidite)	Meandering fluvial Braid plain	River-dominated delta (stacked packages) Meandering fluvial (stacked point bars) Back barrier (stacked packages) Submarine fan (stacked packages)

Figure 3. Depositional environments classified here by variations in heterogeneity in horizontal and vertical directions. After Tyler and Finley (1991). Used by permission.

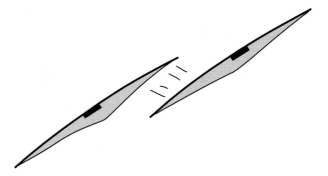

Figure 4. An example of a systematic fault pattern — simple en echelon normal faults with associated relay ramps.

Properties

Textural variations in siliciclastic rocks exert a strong influence on petrophysical properties (including permeability, porosity, and acoustic properties). Grain size and sorting variations occur at several length scales. An awareness of these scales is important when selecting an appropriate sample volume and density. Decisions about sample volume and density of measurements are important first considerations for any geologic

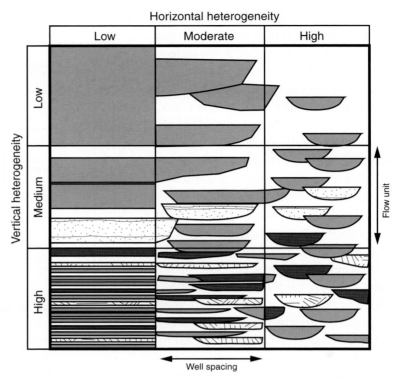

Figure 5. Architectural matrix showing systematic variation of reservoir sand bodies. Horizontal and vertical scales are defined by flow unit and well spacing, i.e., by petrophysical- and engineering-length scales rather than by geologic-length scales. Drilling wells closer together will move the representation of reservoir architectural description closer to the top right of the diagram, and wells farther apart will move the representation toward the bottom left corner. After Tyler and Finley (1991). Used by permission.

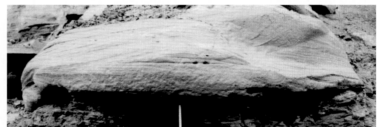

Figure 6. A low-angle cross-laminated set in a shallow-marine reservoir sandstone (Oxfordian Bencliff Grit, Osmington Mills, Dorset). The rule is 10 cm.

modeling study. The statistical properties of support volume and stationarity are critical. Only measurements taken at the homogenization plateaus in the nested hierarchy of length scales will satisfy the support volume and local stationarity conditions for that reservoir volume. Measurements taken at those scales will be effective for simulation. The issue is a challenge in clastic rocks, but the challenge is even greater in carbonates. A comparative laboratory study (Figure 11) illustrates the petrophysical challenge inherent in measuring carbonate rocks.

We can use averages of appropriately measured data to upscale to a different volume scale. This process essentially combines data measured at one homogenization-length scale to predict properties at a larger scale. In laminated or layered systems, we can use the arithmetic and harmonic averages at various scales to examine the variation of the ratio of vertical permeability to horizontal permeability, k_v/k_h, with scale. We see that k_v/k_h clearly is scale dependent and very much a function of the hierarchical geologic architecture introduced in the previous chapter (Figure 15 of Chapter 4).

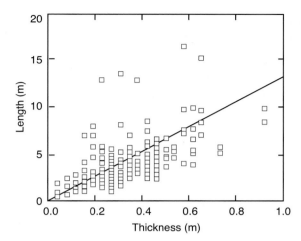

Figure 7. Aspect ratio data for low-angle cross-laminated sets (from Figure 6) in a shallow-marine reservoir sandstone. From Corbett et al. (1994). Reprinted from *Sedimentology*, **41**, 729–745. ©Blackwell Publishing. Used by permission.

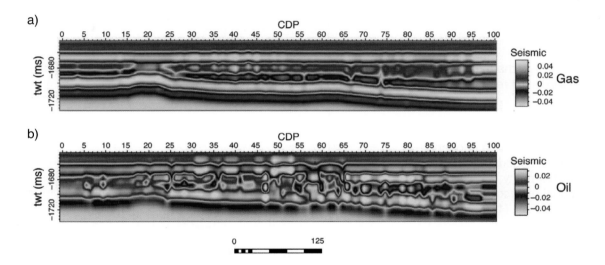

Figure 8. Synthetic seismic data for the Ainsa outcrop sections, using a 30-Hz zero-phase Ricker wavelet to represent typical conditions and properties of North Sea Tertiary sandstones. The same geometry can be used to generate synthetics for other parts of the world (offshore Brazil, Angola, and the Gulf of Mexico) where turbidite reservoirs are important targets. Data courtesy of I. Lopez. Used by permission.

The anisotropy is also facies dependent. The measurement and upscaling of k_v and k_h (and the ratio k_v/k_h) are a challenge. This is illustrated by detailed laboratory studies. In the first (Corbett et al., 1999), a carbonate sample initially was measured with a probe permeameter (at two tip sizes) before being cut into cubes, for which permeability in three orthogonal directions could be measured (Figure 12). The probe data then were averaged (arithmetic, geometric, and harmonic averages) and compared with directional permeability measurements (Figure 13).

In each case, the appropriate upscaling average was close to a geometric average (suggesting a random permeability distribution) or a harmonic average (suggesting flow across a series of layers). Thus, the samples came from very closely spaced locations, illustrating how different the cubic samples were from one another (nonstationary). In the second study (Corbett, 1993), of a laminated clastic reservoir, k_v/k_h clearly varies by scale of measurement and facies (Figure 14). Selecting the right ratio for a model requires close interactions among a geologist, a petrophysicist, and a reservoir engineer.

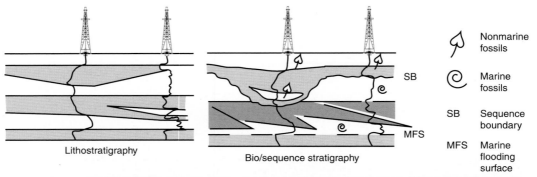

Figure 9. Alternate lithostratigraphic and sequence-stratigraphic models. Use of the latter resulted in additional oil recovery. After Jantschik et al. (1996). Used by permission.

Figure 10. Use of a sequence-stratigraphic model for the Eich field in Germany resulted in additional oil recovery. After Jantschik et al. (1996). Used by permission.

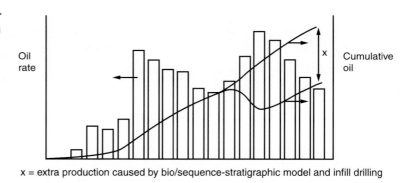

x = extra production caused by bio/sequence-stratigraphic model and infill drilling

Figure 11. Comparison of laminated sandstone and a carbonate with multiple pore types, showing different characteristics of porosity distribution. From Corbett et al. (1999). Used by permission.

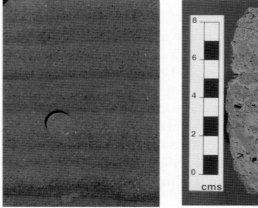

Predictions of k_v/k_h at larger scales can be validated by dynamic measurements in the subsurface. In studies of a mixed fluvial-eolian sequence, Thomas et al. (1997) and Morton et al. (2002) showed that predictions from probe data (Figure 15) from core samples could be upscaled to the same modular-dynamic-tester (MDT) scale. In this approach (Figure 16), the MDT measurements can be used to validate the prediction model.

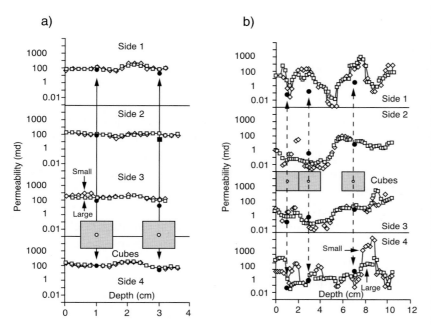

Figure 12. Measurement of (a) a sandstone and (b) a carbonate at two volume scales, using probe-permeameter tips of different radii. This demonstrates good support, and local stationarity is present at this scale of measurement in the sandstone but not in the carbonate. Because of that stationarity, the small-scale measurements match the properties measured at the larger cube scale for the sandstone. This is not possible for the carbonate case (Figure 13). From Corbett et al. (1999). Used by permission.

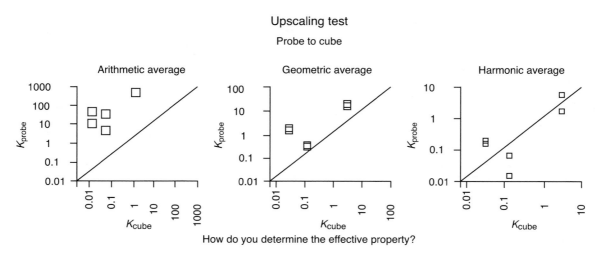

Figure 13. Comparison of cubic cell measurements and averages of local probe-permeability measurements. In this carbonate sample, effective permeability varies between the geometric average and harmonic average. From Corbett et al. (1999). Used by permission.

In each of these examples, the important message is that measurements at different scales are used effectively to predict values at a larger scale, and those predicted values can be validated by dynamic measurements. Careful assessment of the statistical support and stationarity issues is critical to the upscaling and premodel-building phases of a project. Often, the systematic variation of properties within the genetic units can be exploited for efficient sampling and effective scale-up.

Several discrete rock types can exist in a reservoir, and they can be defined by mapping reservoir properties on a global-hydraulic-element (GHE) grid. Capturing the variability at various geologic-length scales should be the priority of petrophysical analysis. With an increased use of time-lapse monitoring, the change of acoustic properties with changes in saturation and/or stress particularly requires measurement of additional properties. In addition, the use of shared-earth models requires that those properties be measured in common samples.

Textural variations in clastic rocks exert a strong influence on petrophysical properties. Grain size and sorting variations occur, as do several length scales. An awareness of those scales is important when selecting an appropriate sample volume and density. Figure 17 shows a comparison of two 10-m intervals, one from a meandering fluvial system and one from a braided fluvial setting.

The variation in permeability detected by a probe permeameter clearly is different in the two intervals in Figure 17 (and can be related directly to textural variations), thereby implying that a different sampling strategy might be appropriate for the intervals. Careful assessment of the statistical support and stationarity are critical to the upscaling and modeling phases of a project. Often, the systematic variation of properties in genetic units can be exploited for efficient sampling and effective scale-up. Capturing the variability at various geologic-length scales should be the priority of any petrophysical analysis.

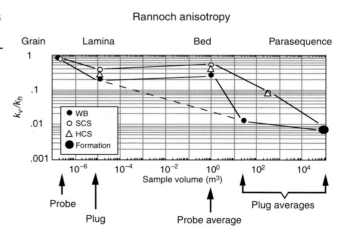

Figure 14. Permeability anisotropy varies in vertical and horizontal directions (k_v/k_h) with increasing volume scale in a shallow-marine sandstone. The Rannoch Formation in the North Sea Brent Group shows variations in k_v/k_h versus volume scale for three facies (WB = wavy bedded; HCS = hummocky cross-stratification; SCS = swaley cross-stratification). From Corbett and Jensen (1993b). Reprinted from *Marine and Petroleum Geology*, **10** (4), P. W. M. Corbett and J. L. Jensen, An application of probe permeametry to the prediction of two-phase flow performance in laminated sandstones (lower Brent Group, North Sea), pages 335–346, ©1993, with permission from Elsevier.

A useful measure of variability is given by the coefficient of variation (CV), which can be determined for any length scale (Figure 18). The CV also is useful because quantification of variability leads to an understanding of sample sufficiency, which can be

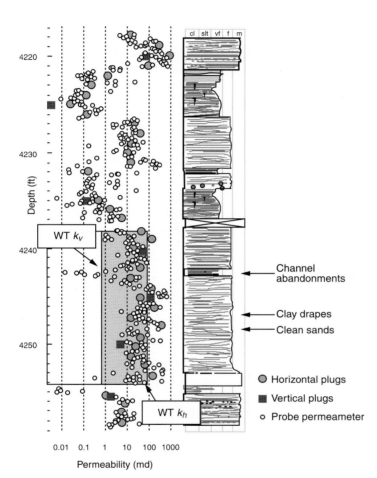

Figure 15. Probe-permeameter data, core-plug data, and a vertical interference well test (WT) in an interval of fluvial sandstone. The vertical pressure response was measured over an interval shown by the gray box in the permeability track. From Morton et al. (2002). Used by permission.

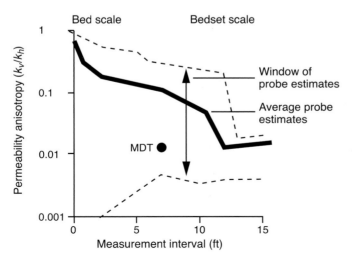

Figure 16. Estimates of k_v/k_h for various subintervals, from arithmetic/harmonic averaging of probe-permeameter data over increasing interval lengths in a fluvial sandstone. The spread of values drops at the thresholds to the different homogenization plateaus. For this total interval, the homogenization-length scale occurs at about 12 ft (4 m). A vertical interference test measurement over this length scale likely would have been more effective for this interval. The actual location, chosen on the basis of image log data, appears to provide a reasonable measurement for the interval. From Morton et al. (2002). Used by permission.

used to drive appropriate sampling density so that one can estimate effective properties within a predefined tolerance — $(10CV)^2$ for tolerance of 20% for sandstone, according to Corbett and Jensen, 1992b, and $(4CV)^2$ for tolerance of 50% for carbonates, according to Corbett and Jensen, 2000.

Figure 19 shows an interval of the Rannoch Formation in the United Kingdom, sampled by probe and plug data. The plug average is 390 md, with a CV of 0.74. The probe data have a lower average and higher variability (average permeability of 172 md and a CV of 0.99). With the 274 probe data, the average permeability is defined within a tolerance as 172 ± 12% md, whereas the plug data give 390 ± 49% md. Tolerance is defined as $200 \times CV/(N^{1/2})$ (Corbett and Jensen, 1992b).

The geoengineer has to decide the target tolerance for a particular study. The more heterogeneous the reservoir is, the more samples are required to capture the average within a certain tolerance. With very heterogeneous reservoirs, the geoengineer might have to accept greater uncertainty.

Sample-sufficiency and sample-volume issues often are overlooked by traditional approaches. Such issues are critical to the underpinning of all future geoengineering studies and should be incorporated into a systematic approach to core sampling.

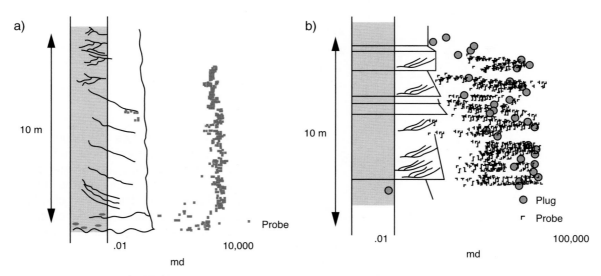

Figure 17. Comparison of length scales of permeability variation for two fluvial systems. (a) For a meandering channel, the variation is dominated largely by the meter-scale vertical variation in a point bar. (b) In contrast, a braided system will show dominant heterogeneity to be at centimeter-lamina and decimeter-bed scales.

Modeling

The simplest method of modeling uses averages for generating upscaled flow properties for a reservoir model. The arithmetic, geometric, and harmonic averages are used to model the horizontal flow in layers of equal thickness, a random system in two dimensions, and the vertical flow in layers of equal thickness, respectively (Archer and Wall, 1986).

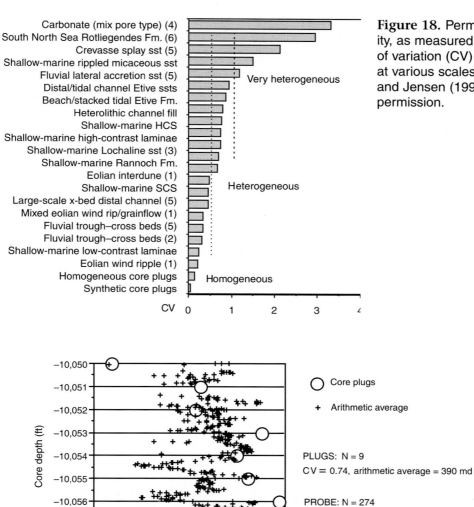

Figure 18. Permeability variability, as measured by the coefficient of variation (CV) for various rocks at various scales. From Corbett and Jensen (1992b). Used by permission.

Figure 19. Comparison of core-plug and probe measurements over an interval of the Rannoch Formation. See text for discussion. From Corbett (1992). Used by permission.

Geostatistical tools have been used increasingly during the last 20 years to populate geologic models (Dubrule, 2003; Coburn et al., 2006). Those tools allow the building of large multicelled models that have equal probability of occurrence for the numerous realizations. Such tools are the only effective way to capture the variability discussed in the previous section.

In addition to variability, spatial correlation also is required, and we already have seen that the multiple hierarchical correlation structure in geologic media poses a challenge for measurement and modeling. The aim of stochastic modeling is to blend deterministic and random components together. The deterministic elements include the probability distribution function (pdf) and the variogram (also called semivariogram) and any fundamental (sequence-) stratigraphic or geographic trends. The geoengineer needs a variety of tools to capture the length scales that affect the engineering outcome. Remember that models, by definition, are always wrong. A geoengineering judgment is what makes some models useful.

The simplest geostatistical models assume stationarity (Figure 20). Nonstationary fields often exhibit trends. The variogram is the usual measure of spatial continuity and can be used to identify data behavior ranging from extreme continuity to complete randomness (Figure 21). Behavior near the origin is captured by a range of variogram functions (Figure 22).

Such geostatistical tools can be used to model a range of permeability fields (Figure 23), and those fields are the basis of 3D pixel models. Those stationary models might represent the geology appropriately at a particular homogenization scale, but they might not capture the multiple-length scales appropriately.

The use of proportion curves (Eschard and HERESIM Group, 1992), shown here in a simple shoreface example (Figure 24), illustrates how progradation of a shoreface body can be used to control vertical distribution of facies proportions in a model. Lateral proportion curves or regions (templates) can be used to control lateral variations in facies proportions.

An alternative to geologic facies modeling is the use of object modeling (Holden et al., 1998), in which the correlation length (variogram) is replaced by a shape that is defined for geologic objects by pdfs for each object that are composed of length, width,

Figure 20. Comparison of stationary and nonstationary fields. From Dubrule (2003). Used by permission.

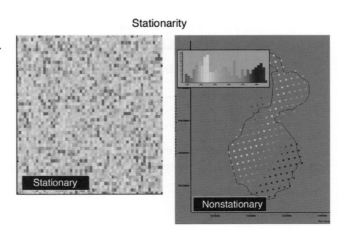

and thickness. Placement rules (Figure 25) ensure that the objects are placed in the model in a geologically correct manner. Those rules can incorporate sequence-stratigraphic trends to build meaningful models. Using a combination of stochastic techniques — both pixel and object techniques — allows the geoengineer to build a range of models for different applications (Figure 26). More specialized tools are available for building bedding-scale geologic models using a combination of pixel and object techniques (Wen et al., 1998).

The information learned from the modeling exercise along with the petroleum-geoengineering judgment of the model's output makes the exercise and models useful. Thus, the geologic modeling stage discussed above must be followed by calibration using independent dynamic or geophysical data. Geologic models calibrated in this manner will be used for predicting flow, stress state, and acoustic response, so such models ideally

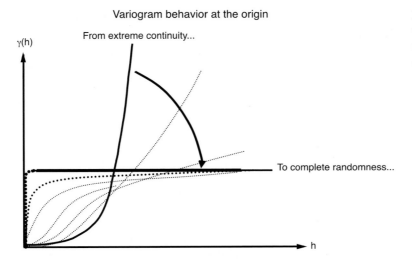

Figure 21. A variogram (semi-variogram) for continuous to random fields. From Dubrule (2003). Used by permission.

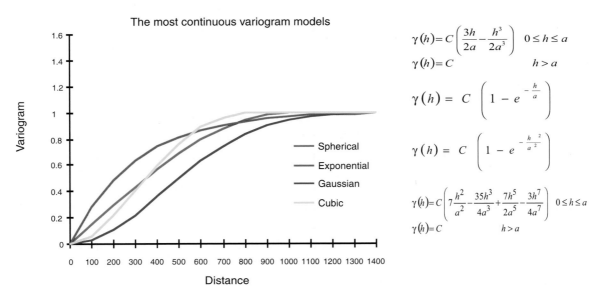

$$\gamma(h) = C\left(\frac{3h}{2a} - \frac{h^3}{2a^3}\right) \quad 0 \le h \le a$$
$$\gamma(h) = C \qquad\qquad h > a$$

$$\gamma(h) = C\left(1 - e^{-\frac{h}{a}}\right)$$

$$\gamma(h) = C\left(1 - e^{-\frac{h^2}{a^2}}\right)$$

$$\gamma(h) = C\left(7\frac{h^2}{a^2} - \frac{35h^3}{4a^3} + \frac{7h^5}{2a^5} - \frac{3h^7}{4a^7}\right) \quad 0 \le h \le a$$
$$\gamma(h) = C \qquad\qquad\qquad h > a$$

Figure 22. Comparison of commonly used variograms. From Dubrule (2003). Used by permission.

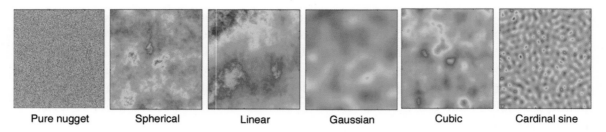

| Pure nugget | Spherical | Linear | Gaussian | Cubic | Cardinal sine |

Figure 23. Models using stationary variograms. From Dubrule (2003). Used by permission.

Figure 24. A simple vertical sequence through a shallow-marine shore-face, showing a systematic change in facies proportions at different levels in the system. The simple proportion curve uses the technique described in Eschard et al. (1992).

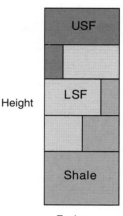

Height

Facies proportions

should involve characterization of depositional and structural elements across a range of scales. Producing and visualizing a 3D geologic model can aid workers in selecting the most appropriate models and in facilitating communication with experts from other disciplines.

Simulation

A simulation phase often is needed to calibrate a geologic model against dynamic production or well-test data so that we can understand the system's dominant drainage mechanism. Figure 27 shows a systematic variation in well-test responses for different radii in a high-permeability region connected to a wellbore. Such synthetic responses can be compared with the real response to select the most appropriate model.

Following such a validation step, the upscaled model is used to simulate longer-term performance of the well and/or field. Upscaling is an important consideration for efficiently capturing the small-scale relevant variability (and, despite ever more powerful computing resources, it is expected to remain so). Various averages (from arithmetic to harmonic means) or numerical functions (e.g., pseudo-relative permeability curves or steady-state upscaling) might be appropriate for capturing the effective interaction between the flow process (fluids) and the rock structure. Simulation is the key to validating geologic models with dynamic data if care has been taken to evaluate and preserve the effects of the detailed model during the upscaling process. The appropriate averaging or upscaling technique often depends on the geologic architecture, so involvement of the geoscientist at the upscaling stage is logical.

Legrand et al. (2007) considered model calibration by well-test data in a field-scale model. Surprisingly to the geologists involved in that study, the model built using a random distribution of facies matched the well-test data (a more layered model). The under-

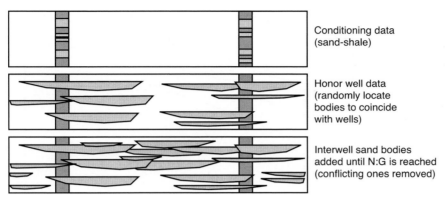

Figure 25. A simple object (channel) system, showing placement of the objects controlled first by well data and then by (stationary) net-to-gross ratio. Note that the channels placed later erode the earlier channels in a manner that replicates their depositional form.

Conditioning data (sand-shale)

Honor well data (randomly locate bodies to coincide with wells)

Interwell sand bodies added until N:G is reached (conflicting ones removed)

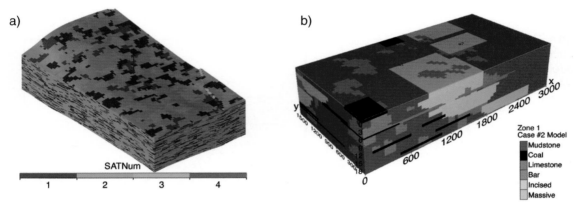

Figure 26. A range of model types can be used to represent different geologic environments. (a) A braided fluvial system is represented by a pixel model of rock types (Yasin Ellabad, personal communication, 2005). (b) A coastal-plain system is represented by an object model of different geologic bodies (Liang Chen, personal communication, 2001).

lying theory would have predicted the geometric average if the researchers had known the geology was random. However, the geometric average did not work across the field, which suggests that the permeability field in that braided fluvial reservoir was nonstationary (Toro-Rivera et al., 1994).

Management

Management issues generally are investigated by various members of an asset team. Database maintenance and access remain important management issues. Integration among disciplines must be effective for challenging and rewarding development plans to be generated, implemented, monitored, and evaluated. The numerous realizations for the appropriate sensitivities (Figure 28) need to be considered against an economic threshold if risk is to be considered appropriately.

Using appropriate petrophysical properties to link depositional architecture to realistic geologic models and then calibrating those models by production data establishes the framework for improved exploitation of a reservoir to maximize hydrocarbon recov-

Figure 27. Type curves from a simple geologic model (with varying radii of the high-permeability region around a well) for comparison with real pressure data Courtesy of T. Kulagina. Used by permission.

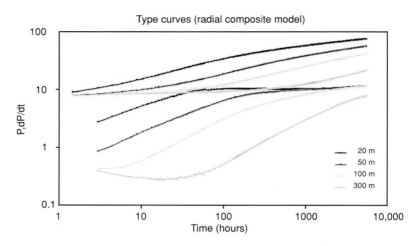

Figure 28. Multiple performance predictions from a modeling exercise. Courtesy of M. Christie. Used by permission.

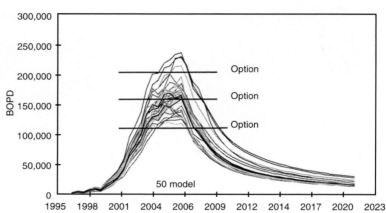

ery. Similar models also might result in less produced water and can be used for disposal (or enhanced recovery by managed injection) of acid gases. A closer understanding of the links among architecture, properties, and recovery factors (Figure 29) will provide a feedback loop and will drive the improvement of global recovery factors.

Summary

With the above-described understanding of the issues that underlie geologic heterogeneity, statistical support and property measurement, and upscaling, we can begin to look at some actual examples.

How does the conventional approach differ from a petroleum-geoengineering approach, which integrates geology, geophysics, petrophysics, and reservoir engineering? The answer lies in a systematic focus of the disciplines toward a common goal and in feedback at each stage as the skills are employed. The next chapter will consider that perspective by using illustrative studies across the range of scales.

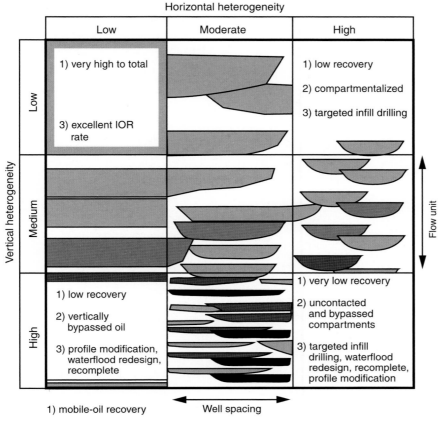

Figure 29. An architectural matrix showing remaining oil, IOR opportunities, and management techniques for improving oil recovery. The graphic matrix (from Figure 5) was derived from Tyler and Finley's original descriptive table (see Figure 3 above). After Tyler and Finley (1991). Used by permission.

Chapter 6   Examples of Petroleum Geoengineering

The challenge that we set in Chapter 2 — to maximize petroleum reserves and to develop our science with an eye toward achieving energy sustainability — can be addressed by applying the geoengineering skills discussed in Chapter 3 to the problem of breadth and integration. Geologic media are hierarchical and have multiple-length scales, so our examples cover scales increasing from pore to reservoir size. Ideally, a systematic geoengineering approach would set out to include all those scales in a new project. At this stage of development for the geoengineering method, studies have focused on individual parts of the problem. However, this work intends to show what might be achieved across all scale sizes, and in so doing, it aims to encourage a more systematic and complete approach to reservoir modeling.

Pore scale

Numerical or digital pore-scale studies have become the norm in certain laboratories, and they allow pore-scale modeling of pore-scale physics designed to predict effective properties at the millimeter scale. Such studies tend to address the specific challenges of two-phase or three-phase flow. However, technology now being developed (the numerical approach to petrophysics often is referred to as "digital petrophysics") will allow us to predict petrophysical and rock-physics properties to supplement and extend the range of limited numbers of measurements. Those modeled measurements are effectively at a fundamental scale because the models tend to be stationary — they are above the microscopic-macroscopic threshold (Figure 1 of Chapter 4) but within a lamina. Geologists define *laminae* as being texturally uniform, so this scale applies to the smallest representative elementary volume in a reservoir. The technology used in such studies combines high-resolution X-ray imaging, geostatistics, and pore-network modeling (Figure 1).

Laminaset scale

Laminae are arranged in laminaset elements in sedimentary rocks. Because of the strong capillary forces that act over a short-length scale, the variation in oil reservoirs in this particular scale length can be significant for reservoir modeling (Corbett et al., 1992; Corbett and Jensen, 1993a; Ringrose et al., 1993; Ringrose and Corbett, 1994; Pickup et al., 1995). Those forces might have significant macrosopic effects and must be assessed in any geoengineering study.

An example in which a laminaset scale of heterogeneity was considered significant is provided by a shoreface reservoir under production in the North Sea (Figure 2). Core data show that the middle-shoreface Rannoch Formation (Middle Jurassic, North Sea) interval comprises hummocky cross-stratification (Figure 3). This interval has well-documented laminaset-scale, bedset-scale, and parasequence (nested) scales of heterogeneity

Figure 1. Pore scale. A numerical pore-scale model used to generate a synthetic pore-size analysis. (a) A binary image is analyzed to create (b) a 3D volume from which (c) an equivalent pore network is extracted. That network can be used to generate (d) a numerical pore-size distribution that can be calibrated by experimental petrophysical data. Courtesy of K. Wu. Used by permission.

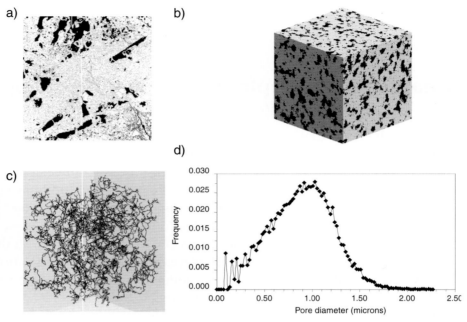

Figure 2. Laminaset scale. Schematic of the Rannoch Formation–Etive Formation flow units between two wells. The engineering question concerns the effectiveness of the waterflood in draining oil from the Rannoch Formation. Because of permeability contrast, the majority of injected water will pass through the Etive Formation and will bypass the Rannoch Formation. The figure is based on a study by Corbett and Jensen (1993b).

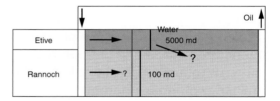

Figure 3. Laminaset scale. The Rannoch Formation is characterized by low-angle cross-laminated stratification (hummocky cross-stratification [HCS]) and swaley cross-stratification [SCS]). Permeability contrasts are at the subcentimeter (lamina) scale in this reservoir unit. The figure is based on a study by Corbett and Jensen (1993b).

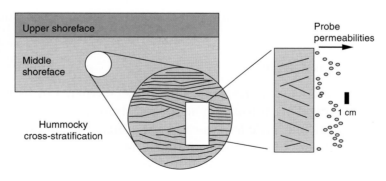

(Corbett, 1992; Corbett and Jensen, 1992a, 1992b; Corbett and Jensen, 1993a; Jensen et al., 1994). Figure 6 of Chapter 5 shows an example of a low-angle cross-laminated sediment.

The issue of concern at the time of the study was how much of the Rannoch Formation was being drained. Sweep efficiency in shallow-marine reservoirs with strong coarsening-upward profiles should be quite effective because the high permeability at the top will take the water. If reasonable vertical permeability exists, the water will drop because of gravity and will sweep the lower-shoreface layers. The Rannoch Formation has a complex k_v/k_h (see Figure 15 of Chapter 5) that shows scale and facies dependency.

Because the principal structure in the Rannoch Formation is small in scale and potentially is dominated by capillary effects resulting from the short-length scale of the variability, careful multiscale upscaling of the effective properties of the Rannoch Formation is required (Figure 4).

The simulation model is matched to the production history (Figure 5). Inspection of the model shows the Rannoch Formation being drained at a lower rate than the overlying Etive Formation. Thus, management can decide whether to drill infill wells to drain the unit more effectively. More recent studies have continued to show that such small-scale heterogeneity can be significant at the reservoir scale (Manzocchi et al., 2008).

The data input to this study relied on information from uniform core plugs assumed to be representative of the laminaset scale. Clearly, with the advent of digital petrophysical data, a seamless geoengineering approach could exist to link the pore-scale and laminaset-scale modeling. High-resolution organic geochemistry can be used at this

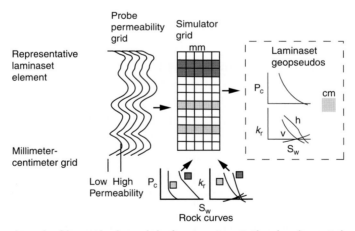

Figure 4. Laminaset scale. Numerical model of a representative laminaset. Input data are in the form of capillary pressure (P_c) and relative permeability (k_r) data (versus water saturation, S_w) from equivalent homogeneous core plugs. The simulation gives an effective-capillary-pressure curve and relative-permeability curves (pseudo functions, or "pseudos") in horizontal (h) and vertical (v) directions for the heterogeneous but representative laminaset elements ("geopseudos"). Reprinted from *Marine and Petroleum Geology*, **10** (4), by P. W. M. Corbett and J. L. Jensen, "An application of probe permeametry to the prediction of two-phase flow performance in laminated sandstones (lower Brent Group, North Sea)," pages 1365–1367, copyright 1993, with permission from Elsevier.

Figure 5. Laminaset scale. The flow-unit simulation containing the effective-flow properties of the laminaset is matched against production data. The figure is based on a study by Corbett and Jensen (1993b).

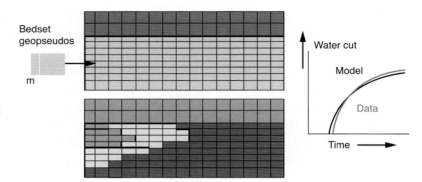

scale to shed additional light on wettability variations in reservoirs at the laminaset and bedset scales (Larter et al., 1997).

Bedset scale

The bedset scale often is referred to as a "missing scale" (Tran, 1996; Caers, 2005) because it is at a scale larger than core-plug data and is not always captured well by wireline data. An example of a bedset-scale approach to characterizing a Jurassic heterolithic tidal reservoir from Norway is provided by Ringrose et al. (2005) and by Nordhal et al. (2005). Heterolithic formations comprise variations in sand, silt, and shale at small scales. The bedforms in this example are composed of flaser and lenticular types with varying discontinuities of mud and sand (Figure 6).

Numerical simulation of a varying shale distribution and empirical calculation of the vertical and horizontal permeabilities allow the effective k_v/k_h to be determined for a range of effective shale volumes (Figure 7). The distribution of those properties in a well then can be controlled by mud volume (Figure 8).

In a further geoengineering step, prediction could be calibrated by a vertical pressure measurement, as was illustrated previously for a fluvial-eolian sandstone (Figures 16 and 17 of Chapter 4) in which discontinuous shale elements also pose challenges for near-well characterization (Morton et al., 2002). Additional well testing also could be used to calibrate predictive permeability models. In the case of vertical-permeability estimation, a carefully designed (partial-perforation) test might be needed. Effective estimation of hydrocarbons in place and recovery optimization in heterolithic reservoirs require a careful predictive model for horizontal and vertical permeability.

A similar scale-up procedure for acoustic properties (using a similar effective-medium theory, with an arithmetic average in thick layers and a harmonic average in thin layers) also would enable use of the sonic log and would link geologic models more effectively to near-wellbore seismic data.

Geobody scale

Well testing (drillstem or production testing) generally is conducted at the geobody scale or larger. Here, a geobody is the single sedimentary element containing the reservoir-property rock (often, a sandstone); a fluvial or deepwater channel would be a typical geobody. Our example, taken from the Middle Jurassic Ness Formation in the North Sea, tests a thin reservoir (Zheng et al., 2000). There are core samples, core data, and a geo-

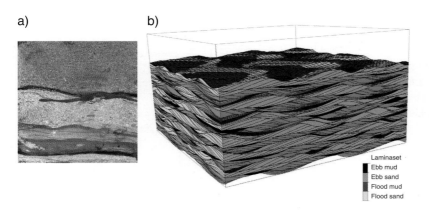

Figure 6. Bedset scale. (a) Heterolithic reservoirs from a tidal sandstone and (b) a reconstruction of the 3D bedform can be used to model this heterolithic facies. From Ringrose et al. (2005). Used by permission.

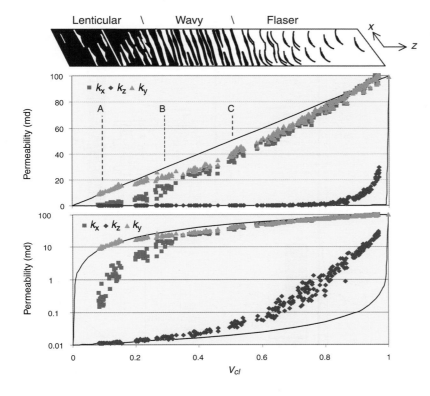

Figure 7. Bedset scale. Effective vertical and horizontal permeability for a variety of shale-sand distributions in a heterolithic tidal sandstone, relating permeability to sand (clastic) volume (V_{cl}). From Ringrose et al. (2005). Used by permission.

logic model for the zone. The pressure-buildup response suggests a complex set of flow regimes. At issue is the effective horizontal permeability.

The core arithmetic-average permeability appears to be higher than the well-test permeability (Figure 9). Probe-permeameter data were acquired to identify that a high-permeability streak is present in the middle of the interval (Figure 10). This streak is associated with a channel base and is thought to be of limited lateral extent. A Lorenz plot of the interval shows that 80% of the flow (i.e., the transmissivity, which is the product of permeability multiplied by thickness, or kh) will come through the interval that represents only 20% of the pore space (i.e., the storativity, or pore thickness, or ϕh) (Figure 10).

This concentration of the flow into the well results in a distinct pressure derivative in the early buildup data (the downhole shut-in data) (Figure 11). The flat middle part of

Figure 8. Bedset scale. Application of the effective-vertical- and effective-horizontal-permeability model for an interval in a heterolithic tidal sandstone. Here, the model relates permeability to mud volume (V_m). From Ringrose et al. (2005). Used by permission.

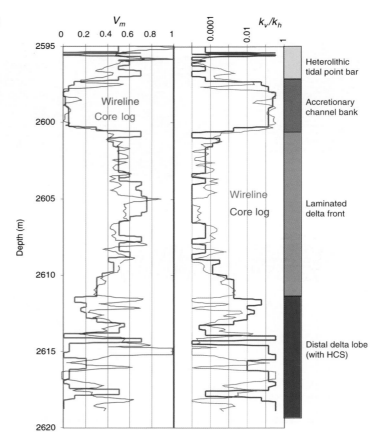

Figure 9. Geobody scale. Example of a short test interval in a fluvial reservoir in which well-test permeability appears not to match core permeability.

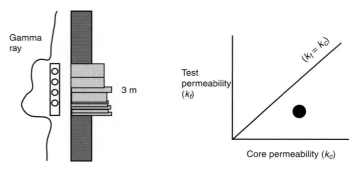

Figure 10. Geobody scale. Detailed analysis of the core using a probe permeameter shows the presence of a high-permeability zone in the middle of the tested interval.

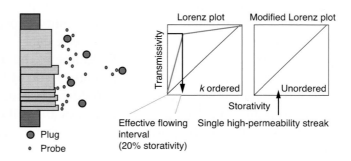

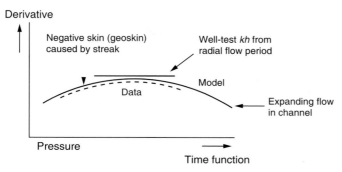

Figure 11. Geobody scale. A distinct pressure derivative indicates a high-permeability zone near the well (the geoskin phenomenon), relative to the well-test effective permeability from the radial plateau. Later pressure data show expanding flow. A numerical model has been used to match the data (Figure 12).

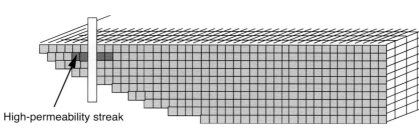

Figure 12. Geobody scale. A numerical model of a high-permeability lag deposit intersecting the wellbore — and giving rise to a negative geoskin — in a channel body that is expanding away from the wellbore.

the buildup data is the radial-flow period from which the value of the test permeability is derived. The late-time data show increasing *kh*. A numerical model of a channel (Figure 12), with a limited high-permeability streak and thickening of the geobody away from the well, gives a good match. From this geoengineering study, we can determine that permeability at the well is enhanced locally by the high-permeability channel base, that the effective permeability in the area of the well is reduced, and that thickness and probably permeability increase as the channel sequence thickens away from the well.

Flow-unit scale

A comprehensive numerical study of the recovery factor in shallow-marine sandstones for a range of shallow-marine shoreface flow units or parasequences (Figure 13) was carried out by the European Union–funded SAIGUP project (sensitivity analysis of the impact of geologic uncertainties on production forecasting in clastic hydrocarbon reservoirs) (Manzocchi et al., 2008). This project built on earlier studies on the significance of geologic heterogeneity on fluid flow (Jones et al., 1993; Kjonsvik et al., 1994). The author list for the SAIGUP summary paper (Manzocchi et al., 2008) neatly captures the breadth of skills and organizations brought to bear in that study.

Despite the resources deployed in the SAIGUP study, the authors are very clear about some of the simplifications made in the 35,000 simulations in the study (Figure 13). There were simplifications to architectural elements (parallel-layered flow units, constant dip and strike), properties (petrophysics, capillary pressure, relative permeability), modeling (pixel-model approach, discrete-fault population), simulation (constant-boundary conditions, mostly vertical wells, simple completions, water injection by voidage

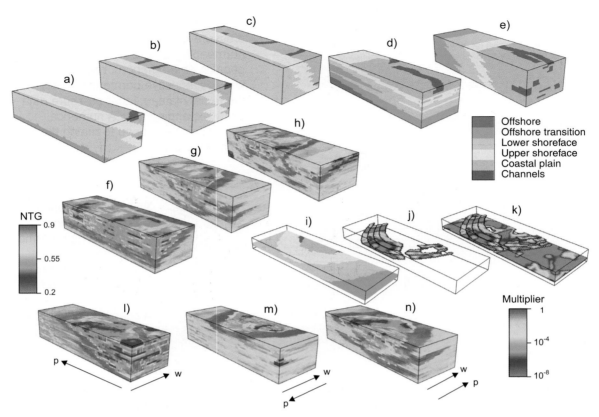

Figure 13. Flow-unit scale. A range of sedimentologic models showing a variety of shallow-marine architectural styles. (a) through (c) Varying parasequence numbers (varying parasequence set size); (d) and (e) varying aggradation rate or stacking pattern; (f) through (h) varying shoreline curvature; (i) through (k) varying cement distributions; (l) through (n) varying waterflood direction. NTG = net:gross. Refer to Manzocchi et al. (2008) for details of all the cases. From Manzocchi et al. (2008). Used by permission.

replacement), and management (limited to recovery factor with no time-lapse seismic results).

From this limited study, certain conclusions were made:

1) The recovery factor ranged from 30% to 55% for this range of models.

2) Large-scale anisotropy, measured by the curvature of the shoreline and aggradation rate in parasequence sets, had a significant effect on the sweep efficiency.

3) Small-scale structure was significant, and the petrophysics (shape of the capillary pressure curve) did have an effect.

4) Simple statistical properties (e.g., the Lorenz coefficient) could be used to indicate the recovery factor — the higher the variability by this measure, the lower the recovery factor (Figure 14).

5) Faulting tends to result in a wider range of outcomes once fault heterogeneity becomes significant (and is sensitive to geometry, density, and properties).

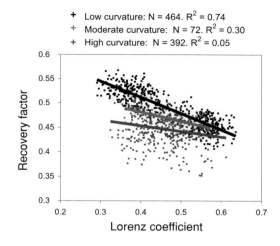

+ Low curvature: N = 464. R^2 = 0.74
+ Moderate curvature: N = 72. R^2 = 0.30
+ High curvature: N = 392. R^2 = 0.05

Figure 14. Flow-unit scale. Correlation between the recovery factor and heterogeneity (which is indicated here by the Lorenz coefficient). The high-curvature models have lower recovery, but the property variability has a controlling effect when the shoreface is more linear. From Manzocchi et al. (2008). Used by permission.

As the authors freely admitted (Manzocchi et al., 2008), this study lacked a reality check but nevertheless points the way to the architectural-element description and property distributions that must be captured to optimize recovery. Reality checks through production data are difficult to combine with synthetic studies because of the uncertainties involved in real case-study data.

However, for us to fully understand the subtle geologic influences (Figure 15) that affect recovery factors throughout the entire spectrum of reservoir types, the level of detail investigated by the SAIGUP study will be required in studies of additional environments. The combination of detailed geologic modeling and a focus on the recovery factor establish the SAIGUP study as a geoengineering study to which all geoengineers should aspire.

Although the same level of detail as that of the SAIGUP study might not be required in every study, the influence of geologic parameters on recovery does need to be understood better so reservoirs can be engineered better for optimal recovery. This has implications for the resources being allocated to geoengineering studies (because the SAIGUP study involved many specialists in different subjects).

A second study at this scale links the modeling of sedimentary architecture and seismic, thereby extending the previous work into the seismic-modeling domain. Rowbotham et al. (2003) developed a workflow that included facies modeling in conditioning seismic-derived porosity maps. A 3D facies model was used (with facies-dependent acoustic-impedance [AI] distributions appropriate for the geomodeling scale) to generate multiple AI realizations (Figure 16). Those realizations were combined with the AI-versus-porosity relationship to produce multiple porosity maps (Figure 17).

That approach integrated the geologic model (with uncertainty in reservoir-layer thicknesses and facies transitions) with the distribution of AI across the facies (which also has uncertainty in the empirical relationships between AI and porosity). In each case, uncertainty in the models — in the geologic, petrophysical, and seismic models — was recognized and treated.

A third study of interest at this scale addressed the modeling of patchy (i.e., subseismic-scale) saturation distributions that developed as a result of production in a similar shallow-marine sequence. In that study, Kirstetter et al. (2006) modeled an outcrop panel

Figure 15. Flow-unit scale. Influential geologic parameters relative to the most influential parasequence-set aggradation angle, for two modeling approaches in the SAIGUP study. From Manzocchi et al. (2008). Used by permission.

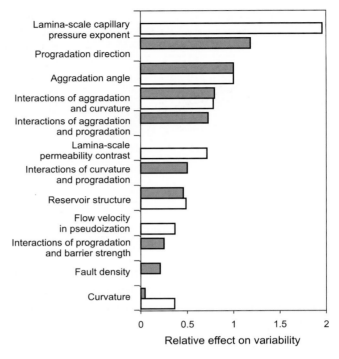

Figure 16. Flow-unit scale. Facies dependency of acoustic impedance (AI) is combined with an appropriate 3D architectural facies model to generate multiple impedance maps. From Rowbotham et al. (2003). Used by permission.

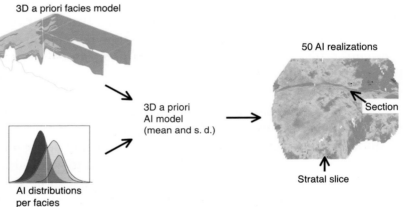

Figure 17. Flow-unit scale. Multiple impedance maps from multiple facies models are combined with a relationship between AI and porosity to generate multiple porosity maps. With the use of collocated cokriging, we can include in the final output the multiple AI realizations based on the 3D geologic model and the variability of the acoustic-impedance (AI)-versus-porosity relationship. That final output might be used to capture variations in pore volume. From Rowbotham et al. (2003). Used by permission.

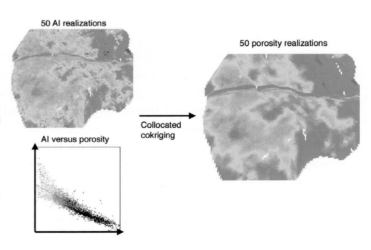

based on photographs from Blaze Canyon, Book Cliffs, Utah, U.S.A., at two scales — a high-resolution geologic-model scale and a more typical reservoir-engineering (upscaled) flow-model scale (Figure 18). Production-related effects, which are of interest in understanding time-lapse responses in geologic systems with complex architectures, were studied at those two scales. The rock-physics data from an analogous sandstone (Figure 19) were combined with saturation distributions from the simulations (Figure 20) to produce impedance sections (Figure 21).

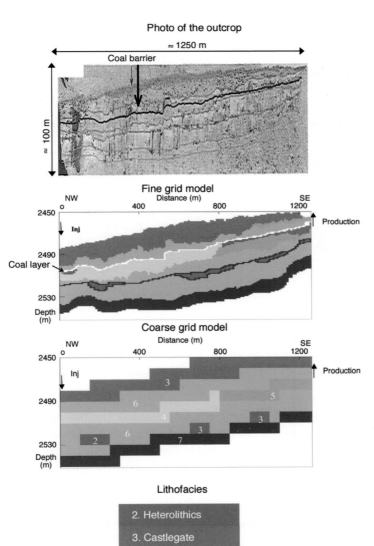

Figure 18. Flow-unit scale. Outcrop-based model of the effects of saturation variation at the parasequence scale. The architecture from the Book Cliffs, Utah, outcrop panel was populated with permeability data from a North Sea reservoir (Rannoch Formation, described in the text above) and rock-physics measurements from another Cretaceous shallow-marine sandstone (Lochaline White Sandstone Formation, Lochaline, west Scotland, Figure 19). The flow simulations are for different production mechanisms to induce subseismic-scale patchy saturation variations (Figure 20). From Kirstetter et al. (2006). Used by permission.

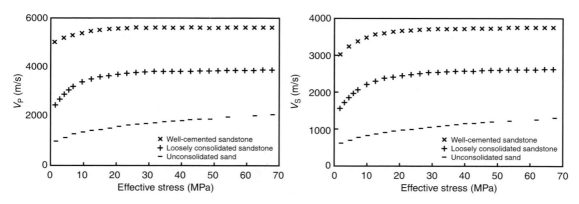

Figure 19. Flow-unit scale. Rock-physics data from the Lochaline Sandstone, west Scotland. From Kirstetter et al. (2006). Used by permission.

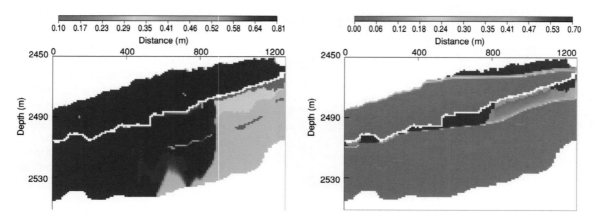

Figure 20. Flow-unit scale. Results of simulations in the Book Cliffs model showing (a) water injection after seven years and (b) gas depletion after 34 years of production. Color scale in (a) is 0.10 to 0.81 and in (b) is 0.00 to 0.70. From Kirstetter et al. (2006). Used by permission.

The effective upscaling of the bulk moduli in the Book Cliffs study (Figure 22) that are used for 4D seismic simulation follow various relationships that can be modeled empirically using empirical elasticity/saturation relationships. For gas injection, the Book Cliffs study found that fine-scale models would be required. To be effective, upscaling acoustic properties requires knowledge of architecture, properties, and simulations for each case. In that way, acoustic properties are not significantly different from relative permeability curves. They both depend on saturation and process and require upscaling for use in a typical simulation model. Seismic models at that scale assist workers in determining influential properties, and the geoengineering approach lends itself to doing that for flow and seismic, at the same time and using the same models.

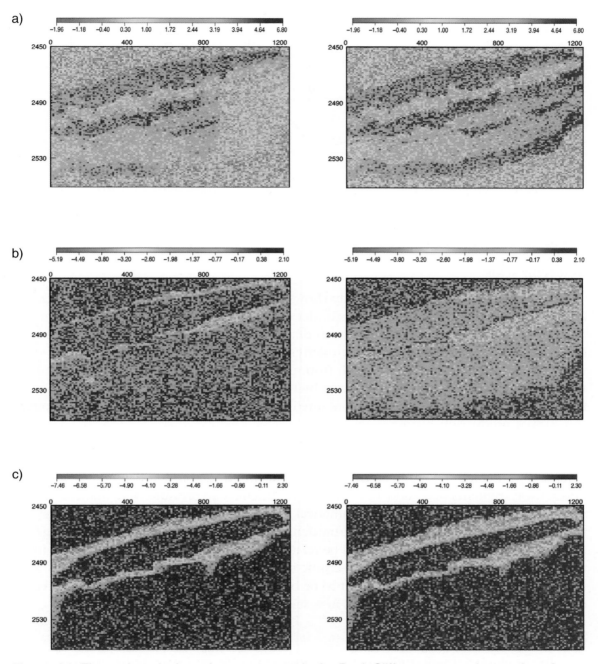

Figure 21. Flow-unit scale. Impedance contrasts in the Book Cliffs outcrop analog section after water injection for seven years and gas depletion for 34 years. (a) Water injection. Color scale (%) −1.96 to 6.8. (b) Pressure depletion. Color scale (%) −5.19 to 2.10. (c) Gas-injection depletion. Color scale (%) −7.46 to 2.30. From Kirstetter et al. (2006). Used by permission.

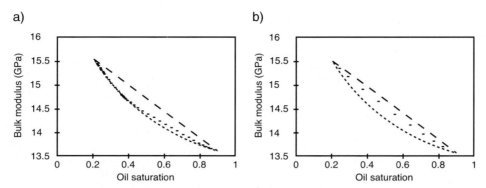

Figure 22. Flow-unit scale. Upscaled bulk moduli for the water-injection case. (a) Fine-grid model. (b) Coarse-grid model. In each case, the solution might be approximated poorly by uniform (Reuss) and patchy (Voigt) bounds. See Kirstetter et al. (2006) for further discussion. From Kirstetter et al. (2006). Used by permission.

Reservoir scale

A large-scale (reservoir-scale) study shows the benefit of integrating seismic data and geomechanics. A gas reservoir was under depletion (Figures 23 and 24) (Olden et al., 2001). The reservoir pressure had been drawn down by 200 bars (20 MPa). There had been no detectable movement of the underlying aquifer water into the gas. At issue was whether detectable effects would result from production (with no saturation changes) — specifically, effects that could be detected by time-lapse seismic, thereby warranting a further survey. The reservoir model contained information on the pressure drop through the 20-year production history (Figure 24).

Because there was concern that the reservoir might have become compacted and stress-related phenomena might be apparent in the overburden, a numerical model was extended to include the latter, along with the side and underburden (Figure 26). Laboratory measurements of V_P and V_S with changes in effective pressure were made of the various lithologies (Figure 25). The numerical model yielded changes in effective stress for the reservoir horizons and the overburden, including details of faults and partings (Figure 26). Those changes then could be related to changes in velocity and density from which "before" and "after" synthetic seismic information could be generated (Figure 27). In this case, the changes were thought to be below the limit for detection, and the recommendation was made not to shoot new seismic for monitoring purposes.

Summary

In conclusion, these studies demonstrate the significant interactions among the scales of property variation and geologic architecture. Such interactions require a geo-engineer to consider carefully the sampling program and the modeling approach as fundamental constraints to the geoengineering method. Key findings are summarized as follows:

1) Heterogeneity can be detected with a probe permeameter (at the lamina scale), core plugs (at the bed scale), or a well test and seismic study at reservoir scales.

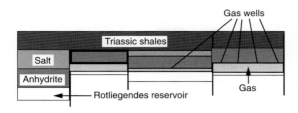

Figure 23. Reservoir scale. Simplified model of a Rotliegendes Formation reservoir (Lower Permian, North Sea). The figure is based on a study by Olden et al. (2001).

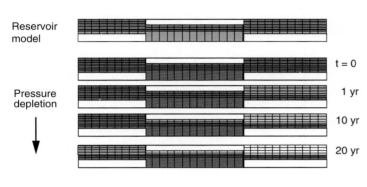

Figure 24. Reservoir scale. Simplified model of pressure depletion in the Rotliegendes Formation reservoir model from Figure 23 through 20 years of production. Fault blocks in the center of the field below the producing platform have been depleted, and fault blocks on the flank remain near original pressure. After Olden et al. (2001). Used by permission.

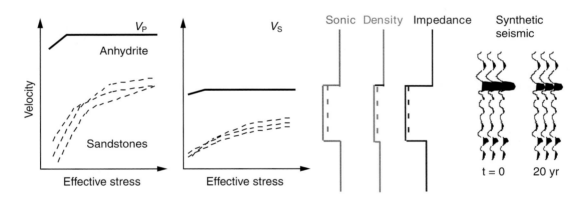

Figure 25. Reservoir scale. Rock-physics and 1D seismic modeling. The figure is based on a study by Olden et al. (2001).

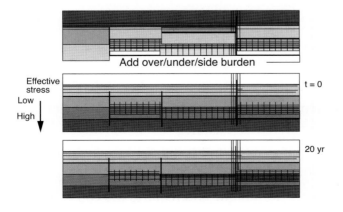

Figure 26. Reservoir scale. Geomechanical/flow simulation for the Rotliegendes Formation model from Figure 23. Side, overburden, and underburden have to be added to the traditional reservoir flow model. In situ stress boundary conditions must be applied. The figure is based on a study by Olden et al. (2001).

Figure 27. Reservoir scale. Synthetic seismic data modeled from the output of the coupled geomechanical-flow simulations. After Olden et al. (2001). Used by permission.

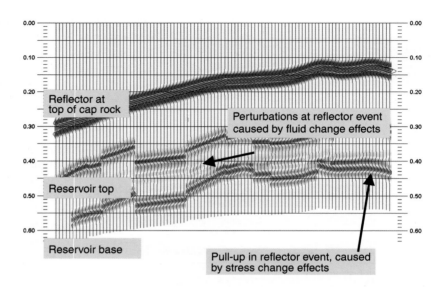

2) Environmental factors associated with air permeabilities (stress corrections, end-point saturation effects) are likely to be second-order effects in heterogeneous reservoirs.

3) Statistical definitions of heterogeneity, such as the coefficient of variation (CV) or the Lorenz coefficient, have been introduced and should be used widely.

4) Sampling rules of thumb have been defined that are based on a level of heterogeneity (for siliciclastics and carbonates).

5) Genetic units and/or stratal elements are the basis of appropriate support volumes in sedimentary rocks rather than samples with fixed physical dimensions (probe, plug, whole core).

6) Cross-scaling and upscaling distinctions help separate physical relationships from the effects of heterogeneity.

7) The number of relative permeability samples is a function of the number of rock types.

8) An effective measurement-strategy design for reservoir description requires an intimate knowledge of geologic heterogeneity and the availability of a range of measurement volumes.

9) Near-wellbore modeling is a critical step in going from core to wireline-log data in heterogeneous reservoirs.

10) Influential geologic parameters can be quite subtle, and systematic geoengineering studies can be employed to tease out those parameters in an exhaustive way.

11) Dynamic data interpretation is inherently nonunique and requires the constraint of the geology.

12) Well-test response is a function of properties and architecture, and those can be bracketed by a set of geotype pressure-response curves (geotype curves are type curves for a family of geologic-model scenarios and/or realizations).

13) Permeability prediction models and geologic models can be calibrated by dynamic data from the wellbore.

14) Numerical well testing allows workers to determine the pressure response to a wide range of geologic structures (architecture and properties).

15) Well-test interpretation is made more nearly unique by use of the Lorenz plot and the modified Lorenz plot, identifying single- and double-matrix-porosity reservoirs.

16) Double-matrix porosity (also known as dual-permeability) behavior is characteristic of braided fluvial reservoir systems. In double-matrix porosity systems, well-test responses show high-permeability "geoskin" effects (a high-permeability zone near the well; Sagawa et al., 2000) and near-well "geochoke" restrictions (the geochoke phenomenon is a restriction of flow, for a short period of time, that represents depletion of high-permeability zones connected to a well and a delay in recharging from other patches away from a well; Corbett et al., 2005).

17) Complex geobodies, such as meander-loop sandstones, can be determined from well-test data.

18) A method has been developed for exploiting the genetic aspects of petrophysics through use of petrophysical analogs. Termed *petrotyping*, the approach has some advantages as a basis for (a) identifying the number of rock types and guiding relative permeability sampling, (b) training neural nets and other predictive tools used for permeability prediction, and (c) systematically mapping property classes by use of a standardized color palette for comparing reservoirs.

19) Fundamental classification of geologic media by petrophysical characteristics (petrotyping) can provide simplification and focus for petrophysical modeling.

In the many studies discussed above, it is currently impossible to illustrate the use of all those techniques in a single coherent study. That remains an aspiration for the future. However, the nature of geoengineering is to design a fit-for-purpose approach to each reservoir challenge.

Chapter 7   The Future for Petroleum Geoengineering

Much work is yet to be done. We need to extend the petroleum-geoengineering workflow to include characteristics of fault patterns, fault properties, and stress sensitivity, and we must model the geophysical response to production so we can improve our predictions of reservoir performance. Certain aspects of reservoir engineering need to be addressed in reservoir-specific challenges — such as the effect of solution seams on vertical permeability (Mohammed et al., 2002). Teamwork also must be taught, trained for, and evaluated (Corbett et al., 2002).

Petroleum-geoengineering students welcome the link between outcrop analogues and reservoir performance in the field. The petroleum-geoengineering philosophy can be applied in training geologic modelers (O. Dubrule, personal communication, 2004). Petrophysical studies can be considered to be petroleum-geoengineering studies also (Worthington, 2005; Corbett et al., 2005). In recent years, senior industry figures (J. Spath, personal communication, 2005) have questioned whether the time is right for engineering geologists or geologic engineers in the petroleum industry.

Geologists have worked for many years with the type concept, using it to make sense of complex and often incomplete data sets. *Lithotype*, *stratotype*, and *nomentype* refer, respectively, to type sections of a lithology, a stratigraphic interval, and a type specimen (of a fossil species). These are published reference specimens — well-visited outcrops or museum specimens — against which new, unidentified examples are compared. In the work in hand, the idea of a reference catalog has been extended to petrophysics (petrotype) and to engineering (geotype) for use in permeability prediction and well-test diagnosis.

 Characteristic combination patterns of global hydraulic elements (GHEs) and dynamic-pressure responses can be diagnostic of a certain type of reservoir and often can be related to the genetic origin within a depositional environment. Used in combination with geologic information, the nonuniqueness of the engineering interpretation can be addressed.

As a student biostratigrapher, the author considered himself to be a "lumper" rather than a "splitter" (Lord et al., 1987). Clustering poroperm data into 10 classes can be seen as a natural extension of the former biostratigrapher's instinct.

Mapping certain characteristics of each reservoir in a systematic way against a global database is defined as *reservoir geonomics* (Corbett, 2002), and it parallels for reservoir studies the manner in which genomics underpins taxonomic classification in the animal kingdom. The future role of a geoengineer will be to populate such a database and blend global analogs with local specifics to maximize hydrocarbon recovery. One can envisage development of "resotypes" — well-documented analogs with complete properties and optimum-recovery strategies. If these analogs ultimately are made available for training through immersive 4D environments, geoengineers of the future can be trained in great numbers.

A geoengineer also can build and investigate systematic and geologically realistic numerical models (rather than specific-reservoir models), which then can be used to develop new screening tools based on critical parameters. For instance, the aspect ratio of sandstone bodies relative to well spacing can be an important parameter for any systematic reservoir-engineering guidelines relating an optimal-recovery mechanism to geologic variability (Henson et al., 2002). To date, such studies have been limited largely to academia, but geoengineering departments in companies ultimately could extend this activity into mainstream estimation of resources and reserves.

Various researchers have considered hydrocarbon-recovery factors as a function of depositional environment. Tyler and Finley (1991) showed relationships among recovery efficiency, drive mechanism, and depositional environment. They emphasized that the architecture of the systems rather than the environment per se was an important influence on recovery factors. Larue and Yue (2003) reviewed several databases in a study that focused on recovery from deepwater reservoirs. Their study was unable to capture a relationship between recovery factor and depositional environment. They noted that the databases, which often were built from a geologic standpoint, would benefit from including more details of permeability heterogeneity and of other production and fluid properties.

It is said that the herein-described double-matrix-porosity reservoirs (i.e., reservoirs that have mixtures of high-permeability layers and cross flow, as opposed to those that have double porosity or matrix plus fracture) are the most challenging to manage (Arnold et al., 2004). At the 2008 SPE Applied Technology Workshop on reservoir layering, Antony Maris (vice president for operations at SOCO International) commented that "layered reservoirs highlight the lack of integration more than any others" (A. Maris, personal communication, 2008).

One feels logically that a workflow and database that include useful geoengineering tools and parameters — such as a Lorenz plot, modified Lorenz plot, single- versus double-matrix-porosity reservoirs, cross flow versus commingled layers, range and distribution of GHEs, aspect ratios of sand bodies relative to well spacing, and so forth — might provide additional insights into the controls that determine recovery factors in these complex systems. At the same SPE Applied Technology Workshop on reservoir layering, Ben Stewart of Halliburton/Easywell stated, "Optimizing recovery from layered reservoirs is the new reality" (B. Stewart, personal communication, 2008). To optimize management of such reservoirs — which contain significant unrecovered oil — the industry needs to promote a more integrated geoengineering approach.

Chapter 8   World Oil Reserves and the Potential Prize for Global Petroleum Geoengineering

World oil reserves are estimated variously as being between 1850 and 3012 gigabarrels (Gb), or 10^9 barrels — that is, 1.8 trillion to 3.0 trillion barrels — according to the U. S. Geological Survey (USGS), as quoted in Deffeyes (2001). Deffeyes (2001) projects 2000 Gb from current production figures (Table 1). Peak oil production will occur between 2006 and 2021, according to the Association for the Study of Peak Oil and Gas (ASPO, 2002), at which time it is expected that approximately half the world's "easy-to-produce" oil will have been produced. Other estimates by the USGS have shown total world hydrocarbon reserves to be as high as 7000 Gb.

Can improvements in recovery factor help delay the decline of oil production? Few publicly available data exist for oil-production decline rates, but such declines are thought to be generally rapid once the peak has been reached (Simmons, 2004). It is harder to find figures for global recovery factors. Manoelle Lepoutre of Total reported a global recovery factor of 30% to 40% (M. Lepoutre, personal communication, 2006); Usman Ahmed of Schlumberger reported 37% (Ahmed, 2004). Leif Meling of Statoil, in a paper presented at the World Petroleum Congress (Meling, 2004), gave a present average field recovery of 29% and stated that with improved oil recovery, that figure might rise to 38%, thereby giving a growth of 600 Gb in reserves (based on a statistical analysis of 8600 oil fields). The 9% improvement in recovery factors is certainly a prize worth going after.

Table 1. Current reserves combined with estimated recovery factor to give estimates of world oil resources. Improved-recovery factor from IOR has been applied to these resources to give potential reserves. The upside is then given in years (based on 2003 production and 2020 International Energy Agency [IEA] estimates of world production given by Holditch, 2003).

Estimates	Campbell (2004)	Deffeyes (2001)	USGS
Estimated reserves (Gb)	1850	2000	3012
Recovery factor (%)	29	29	29
Resources (Gb)	6379	6897	10,386
IOR (%)	38	38	38
Potential reserves (Gb)	2424	2621	3947
Upside (Gb)	574	621	935
World oil production (Gb) (2003)	26	26	26
Upside (years)	22	24	36
World oil production (Gb) (2020)	43	43	43
Upside (years)	13	14	22

Each percentage-point improvement in the global recovery factor equates to one-and-a-half to four years' worth of oil production. If we could improve the world's oil-recovery factor to a global average of 45%, then perhaps we could extend the world oil supply by 25 years. In the same vein, Shell quoted that an extra oil recovery of 10% would extend petroleum supplies by 20 years. That is a prize worth pursuing through closer integration of reservoir geoscience and petroleum engineering. Heinburg (2003) noted that virtually all authors who have contributed to the literature on sustainability suggest that society will have to take a more systematic approach to resource depletion, and that implies a more systematic approach to monitoring recovery factors.

What particular reservoirs should we target for improved oil recovery? For North Sea reservoirs, Figure 1 might provide insight. In the North Sea, much of the improved oil recovery shown in the figure might have been achieved already by effective water-injection programs (average oil recovery for reservoirs in the Norwegian sector is said to be greater than 50%). However, a comparable potential in similar reservoir situations around the world must exist. By analogy, one can attribute remaining potential in U. S. Gulf Coast reservoirs to certain reservoir types (Figure 2). BP has introduced a major project on reservoir technical limits (Smalley et al., 2007) that seeks also to push the limits of recovery upward in a systematic way.

Figure 1. Improved-recovery targets in North Sea fields. The darkened bars represent increases that could be achieved through improved oil recovery (IOR), realized in part by the effects of water-injection recovery, illustrated in the upper part of the diagram.

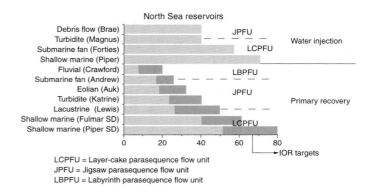

Figure 2. Improved-recovery targets in U. S. Gulf Coast reservoirs. WD = water drive; SG = solution-gas drive. Adapted from Tyler and Finley (1991). Used by permission.

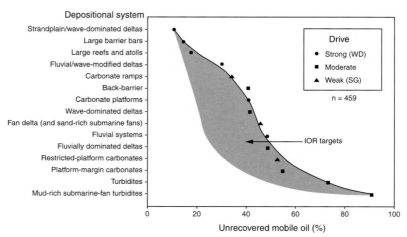

Many of the targets identified are in reservoirs of moderate horizontal and vertical correlation lengths. Such reservoirs commonly are cross-flow reservoirs (Figure 3), which are recognized as being the most difficult reservoirs in which to improve oil recovery (Arnold et al., 2004). They are also reservoirs in which undrained mobile oil potential must be highest. To target these additional reserves in cross-flow reservoirs, integration of geoscience and engineering is required from the start of development, and that is the prize for closer cooperation that is implicit in the petroleum-geoengineering approach.

The work of Weber and van Geuns (1990) and Tyler and Finley (1991) started the trend of linking architecture and recovery for simplified reservoir systems. The layer-cake, jigsaw, and labyrinth flow units of Weber and van Geuns form the diagonal from top left to bottom right of Tyler and Finley's cube (Figures 3 and 5 of Chapter 5). In the present work, the designation of global hydraulic elements (GHEs) as a fundamental breakdown of the petrophysical classes (Figure 4) allows distinction of single-GHE (i.e., single-matrix), double-GHE (double-matrix), and multiple-GHE/matrix reservoirs.

Heterogeneity measures (using the coefficient of variation [CV]; see Chapter 5) suggest that the GHE elements essentially should be uniform (certainly so if the porosity range is limited). Combining single- and double-porosity elements with the Tyler and Finley square provides a systematic framework for well-test interpretation (called the geo-type catalog; see Figure 5).

If we extend this reservoir classification by using geonomic considerations for properties (refer to Chapter 7) — that is, by using GHE and GHE combinations — we can set up a more systematic classification of reservoirs (Figure 6). This also could be represented as a cube. Systematic target-recovery factors for each of the reservoir types can be

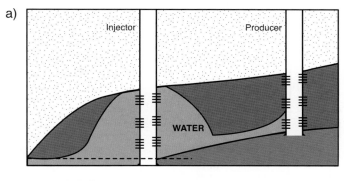

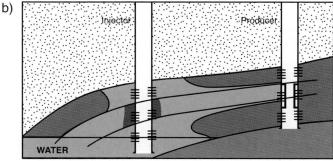

Figure 3. Sweep efficiency (a) with gravity segregation and (b) in reservoirs with high-permeability layers and cross flow. These are some of the most challenging reservoirs in which to try to improve oil recovery. From Arnold et al. (2004). Copyright © Schlumberger, Inc. Used by permission.

Figure 4. The petrotype approach to determining rock types. See Chapter 7 for more discussion on petrotyping and geotyping.

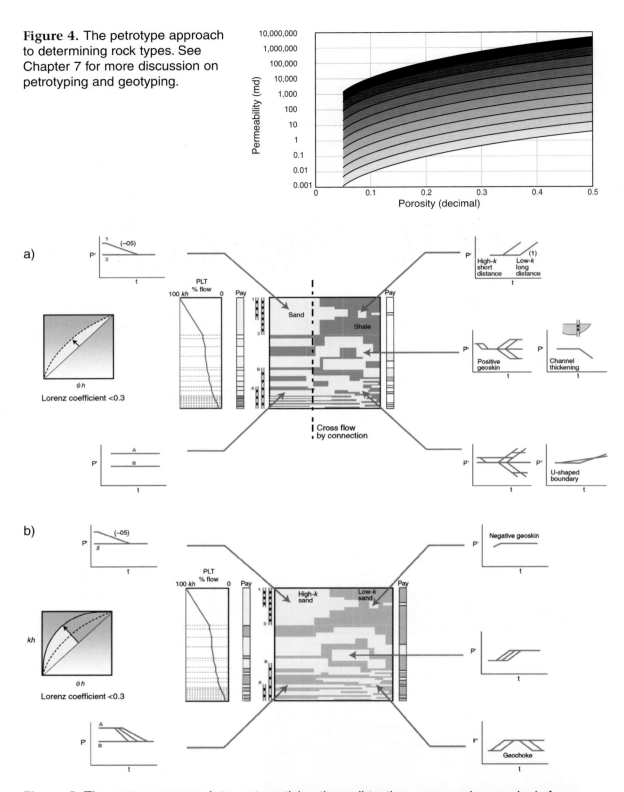

Figure 5. The geotype approach to systematizing the well-testing response in a geologic framework derived from the Tyler and Finley cube. (a) Single-porosity reservoirs. (b) Double-matrix-porosity models. PLT = production logging tests. From Corbett et al. (2005). Used by permission.

assigned on the basis of the recovery factors described above. If industry is going to use this classification widely, these targets can become verified, modified, and monitored.

Recovery targets can be used to drive up reservoir performance and increase worldwide recovery factors. Future work will be needed to populate the systematic catalog with specific reservoir case studies. Additional geologic considerations, such as fracturing, faulting, stress, and fluid properties, doubtless will need to be considered in more detail than they have been so far. Such geonomic parameters might increase the dimensions of the problem, and the systematic framework then could be extended to include them (creating, from the matrix shown in Figure 6, a 5:1 heavy, as opposed to a 5:1 light; a 5:1 faulted versus a 5:1 unfaulted; or a 5:1 stress-sensitive versus a 5:1 not-stress-sensitive characterization).

The SAIGUP study discussed in Chapter 6 is the sort of systematic study that is needed to populate this matrix. Perhaps the reservoirs those workers studied (see Figure 13 of Chapter 6) were in the 2:3 to 4:3 class or the 4:2 to 6:2 class. One look at the size of the SAIGUP project team (Manzocchi et al., 2008) indicates just how much work has to be done by the industry. Note, however, that nobody will recommend that scale of study on every reservoir.

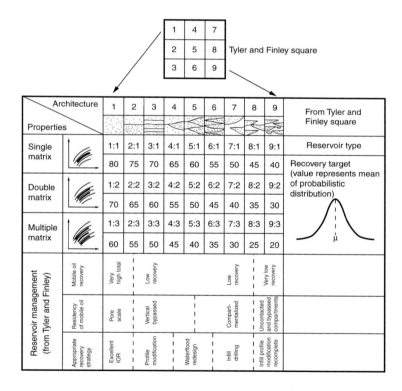

Figure 6. A matrix of systematic architectures and GHEs versus target-recovery factors and reservoir-management techniques. This matrix requires calibration by many systematic geoengineering studies. The diagram needs to be used with caution until the full complexity of architecture and property distributions can be mapped out.

Chapter 9   Conclusions

Petroleum geoengineering is defined as the systematic measurement, interpretation, and modeling of geologic media for the purpose of engineering the earth's subsurface to exploit petroleum reservoirs optimally. In preparation for an engineering decision and ultimately for an engineering implementation, the petroleum-geoengineering workflow (Figure 1) proceeds from a geologic model to the use of petrophysical measurements in a numerical model that simulates outcomes.

Petroleum geoengineering addresses several challenges. In applying this approach, the linkages among reservoir descriptions — both static and dynamic — with feedback loops ensures that the appropriate data are collected and are used in building the model. The ultimate intended use will influence the type of data acquired, and the engineering validation of the geologic model will improve geologic understanding.

Measurement of reservoir parameters is a joint geoscience and engineering challenge because reservoir heterogeneity is nested inherently at various scales (Figure 2), and sampling strategies must distinguish cross-scaling relationships from upscaling issues.

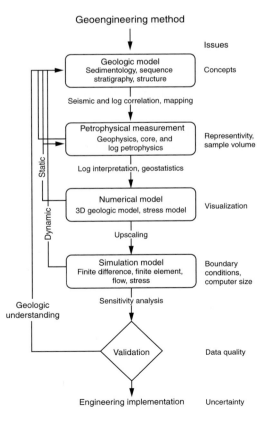

Figure 1. The petroleum-geoengineering method is a workflow from a geologic model to engineering implementation, with feedback at every stage.

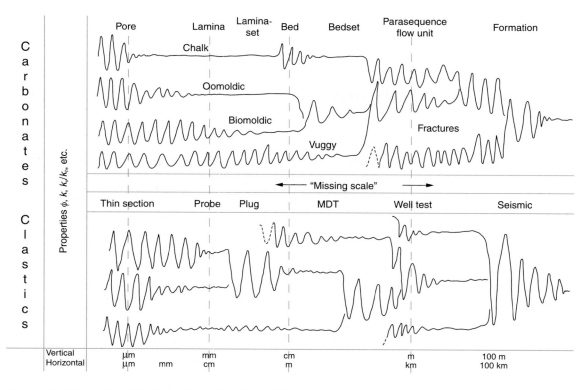

Figure 2. The hierarchical nesting of scales of heterogeneity in carbonates and clastics and the petroleum-geoengineering approach to measurement and upscaling to address the missing scales (as described by Caers, 2005). Siliciclastics have better-defined scales of homogenization, implicit in the hierarchical stratal elements identified in sequence-stratigraphic studies, than often is apparent in carbonates (represented here as fractured systems).

Systematically upscaling laboratory measurements to in situ pressure interference and well tests helps geoscientists to address the missing scales of data in petroleum-engineering studies. Sampling strategies should consider the concept of sample sufficiency to account adequately for the natural heterogeneity of many reservoirs. Compared with siliciclastics, carbonates are more variable and have less apparent intervals of homogeneity for the engineer to exploit.

The nested scales of heterogeneity, often subseismic in scale but generally larger than core-plug scale, are considered to be the missing scales in reservoir descriptions (Figure 2). At such scales, a more systematic approach to modeling and measurement is required. Such modeling and measuring use samples taken at representative volumes. The models then employ different techniques to upscale for model validation, which is done by using measurements acquired systematically at large scales.

A reservoir model needs only a limited number of rock types. Classification of a maximum of 10 global hydraulic elements (GHEs) satisfies the need for reservoir elements and layers (combinations of elements) to be significantly different so as to impact reservoir performance. To improve permeability prediction, petrotyping can exploit characteristic patterns of GHE combinations that are a function of the depositional environment.

Interpretation of dynamic data is not unique, and geologic models and petrophysical tools have been developed to distinguish between reservoir types of single-matrix porosity and double-matrix porosity. Well-test data can be used to diagnose the degree of cross-flow behavior as distinct from commingled behaviors, and that information is important for future oil-field management and recovery optimization.

Petroleum geoengineering also is defined as the petroleum industry's optimal exploitation of the subsurface environment to achieve improved oil-recovery factors on a global scale. Future petroleum geoengineers will have a broad range of geoscience and engineering skills, with appropriate knowledge in the key aspects described in this book. Those workers potentially can develop additional screening tools and maintain reference data sets that will underpin a more systematic approach to reservoir development. In addition, petroleum geoengineers will be motivated to improve hydrocarbon-recovery factors on a global scale to meet the demand for extending hydrocarbon supplies.

Appendix A   Exercise 1: An Upscaling Example

This example is based on the interpretation of two wells, A and B, in a braided fluvial reservoir (Toro-Rivera et al., 1994). The reservoir unit is Triassic and is approximately 90 m thick in each well. The wells are more than 1 km apart in the same field.

Starting with core data from wells A and B (Figure A-1), the reader is asked to select which of the averages is the appropriate one for an upscaled measurement of effective permeability (k_{eff}). To do this exercise, begin with the following useful steps:

1)   Determine net:gross.

2)   Consider sorting by viewing the range of poroperm data.

3)   Consider geometry away from the well location.

4)   Use analog geobody-geometry data (outcrop, well-test data).

5)   Consider assumptions on using averages to estimate effective permeability.

Note that the linear scale (Figure A-1) is a good one for considering the distribution of high-permeability zones. The linear scale is more appropriate than the logarithmic scale (Figure A-2) for that purpose because the fluid flow in reservoirs is controlled by permeability rather than by the log of permeability.

Note also that the logarithmic scale of permeability is always a good scale on which to consider net:gross. For this exercise, take 1 md as the appropriate cutoff for an oil field. Crossplots of porosity and permeability also are provided (Figure A-3). Next, consider

6)   the textural variations expected in this environment and how you might interpret the wells in terms of layers or channels

7)   whether the distribution is systematic or random

Three averages can be used for estimating effective properties. Their application depends on various assumptions. For single-phase flow in two dimensions, use

*   arithmetic average — for a layered system, with layer-parallel flow
*   geometric average — for a random system flow
*   harmonic average — for a layered system, with layer-series flow

Additional information is available from a fluvial-outcrop analogue (Figure A-4) and a subsurface analogue (Figure A-5).

8) Now sketch the geology away from the wells on the templates provided (Figure A-6), and consider the most appropriate average.

Figure A-1. Two wells show the distribution of permeability on a linear scale.

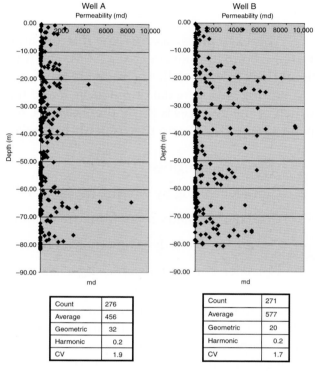

Figure A-2. Two wells show the distribution of permeability on a logarithmic scale.

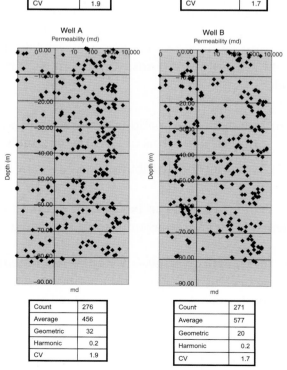

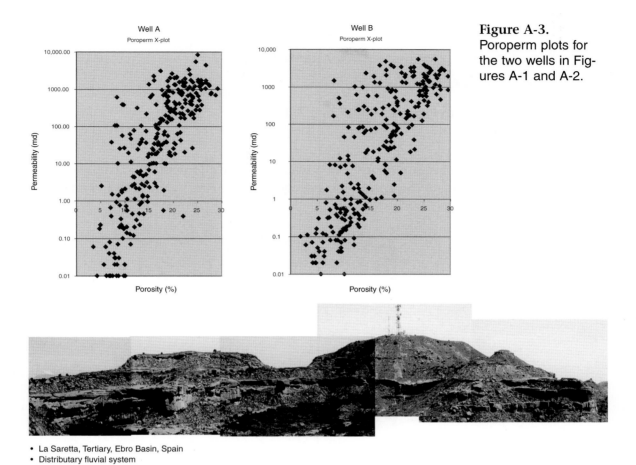

Figure A-3. Poroperm plots for the two wells in Figures A-1 and A-2.

- La Saretta, Tertiary, Ebro Basin, Spain
- Distributary fluvial system
- Vertical/lateral stacked sand bodies
- Medium NTG (35–45%)
- Aspect ratio histogram (log normal, average thickness 5.3 m, average channel width 125 m, average aspect ratio 1:27)

Figure A-4. Outcrop analogue for this exercise, from Spain.

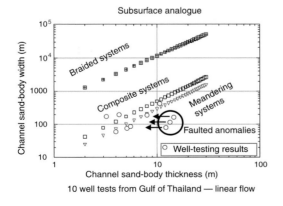

10 well tests from Gulf of Thailand — linear flow

Figure A-5. Subsurface analogue for this exercise, from the Gulf of Thailand. From Zheng (1997). Used by permission.

Given these data, consider the following additional aspects:

9) how well the core plugs describe the heterogeneity

10) an estimation of k_v/k_h anisotropy

For the solutions, refer to Figures A-7 through A-10.

Solutions

With core-plug data, sample-sufficiency issues must be addressed. To acquire enough samples to estimate the arithmetic average within ±10% of the true arithmetic

Figure A-6. Model template for the region around wells A and B.

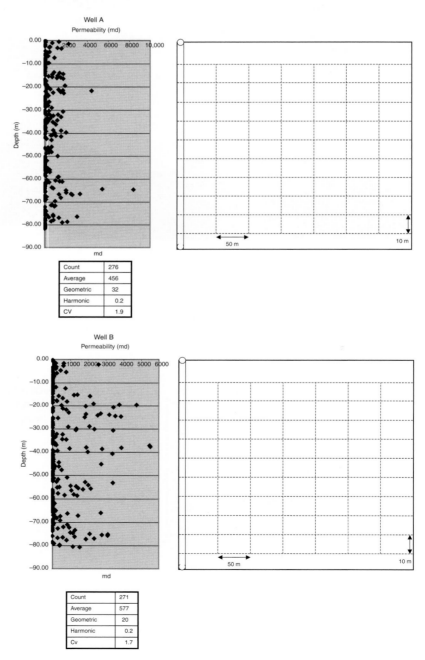

Count	276
Average	456
Geometric	32
Harmonic	0.2
CV	1.9

Count	271
Average	577
Geometric	20
Harmonic	0.2
Cv	1.7

mean (and with a confidence interval of 95%), you need $(10CV)^2$ samples. For wells A and B, these sample sizes are 361 and 289, respectively, which equates to 23% and 21% tolerance for the mean. In this example, one could conclude that the core samples do a reasonable job of catching the variability (assuming there is no bias and the lower-permeability zones are missed systematically).

Figure A-10, a crossplot for vertical permeability (k_v) versus horizontal permeability (k_h) from core-plug data, demonstrates that significant variability occurs at the core-plug

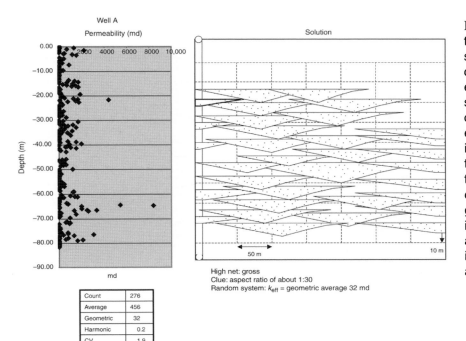

Figure A-7. Solution to well A. Only samples from small channels are present in the core, suggesting that channels of limited extent are present in the region around the well. Because of the random nature of the channels, the geometric average is the appropriate average for estimating effective permeability.

High net: gross
Clue: aspect ratio of about 1:30
Random system: k_{eff} = geometric average 32 md

Count	276
Average	456
Geometric	32
Harmonic	0.2
CV	1.9

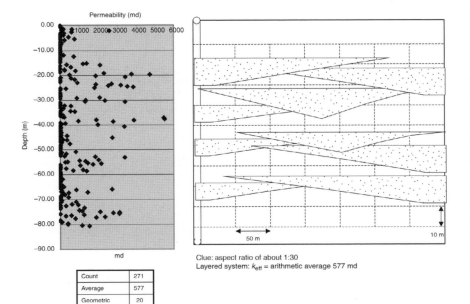

Figure A-8. Solution to well B. A few samples from large channels are present in the core, suggesting that channels of greater lateral extent are present in the region around the well. Because of the layered nature of the channels, the arithmetic average is the appropriate average for estimating effective permeability.

Clue: aspect ratio of about 1:30
Layered system: k_{eff} = arithmetic average 577 md

Count	271
Average	577
Geometric	20
Harmonic	0.2
CV	1.7

scale. Those plugs are adjacent pairs, and variability in the ratio shows much local heterogeneity rather than anisotropy. Considering the models developed above, the layered system (well B) would have the worst-case vertical permeability (as low as the harmonic average of 0.2 md). In a random system, the vertical permeability would be closer to the geometric average, and the system would be effectively more isotropic. This example is shown to draw attention to the difficulty inherent in estimating effective vertical permeability because of the differences of scale. The layering (or lack thereof) of the system will have the major effect.

Figure A-9. In the alternative solution to well A, the channels effectively are not connected and the effective flow is across the interchannel material, which could be very low — possibly as low as the harmonic average.

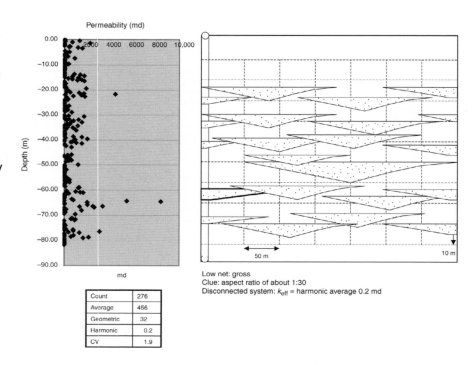

Count	276
Average	456
Geometric	32
Harmonic	0.2
CV	1.9

Figure A-10. Core-plug k_v:k_h (Note that k_v is plotted on the *y*-axes and k_h on the *x*-axes) for wells A and B in this exercise.

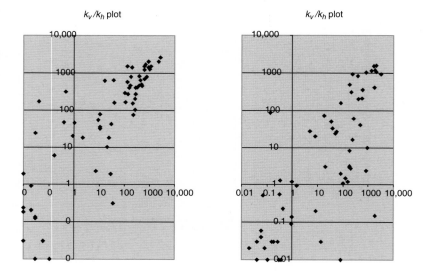

Appendix B   Exercise 2: Reservoir Management

This exercise examines the role of the Lorenz plot and the stratigraphically modified Lorenz plot (Gunter et al., 1997) in reservoir management. We will consider likely reservoir management issues, using the permeability data given in Tables B-1 through B-3 from three wells (for simplicity, each reservoir data set contains 10 layers of equal thickness). To do this exercise, you will need to plot

1)   a Lorenz plot (LP)

2)   a modified Lorenz plot (MLP)

The two plots can be used jointly to examine production characteristics and expected sweep efficiency of the three reservoirs. The prediction of sweep efficiency also will require a model for the lateral extent of the layering. Well-testing information (as used in exercise 1, Appendix A) also can help to inform our discussion of lateral extent of the layers. That knowledge is critical to understanding sweep.

Well A: A fluvial reservoir

The ordered Lorenz plot (Figure B-1a) shows significant heterogeneity. Average permeability is 818 md, and the coefficient of variability (CV) is 1.89. The modified (also referred to as *unordered*) LP (Figure B-1b) shows speed zones in a few locations. This reservoir is a composite sand body, perhaps of braided fluvial origin. If cross flow occurs, this

Table B-1. Porosity and permeability data for well A, in a fluvial reservoir.		Table B-2. Porosity and permeability data for well B, in a turbidite reservoir.		Table B-3. Porosity and permeability data for well C, in a shallow-marine reservoir.	
Porosity (%)	**Permeability (md)**	**Porosity (%)**	**Permeability (md)**	**Porosity (%)**	**Permeability (md)**
0.08	0.05	0.20	100	0.180	500
0.20	30	0.25	1000	0.150	2000
0.20	1000	0.22	500	0.180	200
0.18	5000	Shale		0.175	100
0.10	0.1	Shale		0.170	50
0.08	0.05	0.18	10	0.150	20
0.20	100	0.22	500	0.140	8
0.25	1250	Shale		0.140	4
0.30	800	0.21	80	0.130	2
0.13	3	0.18	20	0.120	0.5

profile will be sustained. Note in Figure B-2 that the reservoir contains six global hydraulic elements (GHEs) and has a range of rock types typical of braided fluvial reservoirs (such as the reservoir we saw in Appendix A). The sweep might not be good because there is a tortuous pathway through the reservoir (Figure B-3).

Figure B-1. (a) Lorenz plot and (b) modified Lorenz plot for well A (in a fluvial reservoir), using porosity and permeability data from Table B-1.

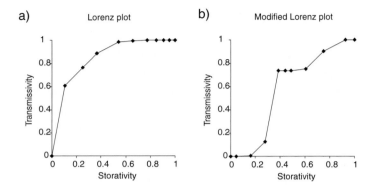

Figure B-2. Petrotype base map for well A, using porosity and permeability data from Table B-1.

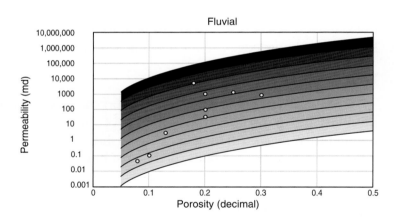

Figure B-3. Lorenz plot and modified Lorenz plot, showing various sweep scenarios depending on continuity of the layers. This fluvial example is similar to the one in exercise 1, Appendix A, in which well B had a longer correlation length than did well A. In that example, the sweep also might be better in the region of well A.

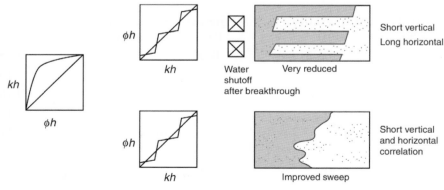

Well B: A turbidite reservoir

The ordered Lorenz plot (Figure B-4a) shows significant heterogeneity in this case also. Average permeability is 316 md, and the CV is 1.17. The modified LP shows speed zones (Figure B-4b) that might be commingled layers because they are separated laterally by shales. Four GHEs are in this reservoir (Figure B-5), i.e., the reservoir is less heterogeneous than is the previous, fluvial example.

The higher-permeability zone will water out first because cross flow is unlikely in the reservoir (assuming a layered architecture of a distal layered turbidite system). That will lead to poor sweep efficiency (Figure B-6).

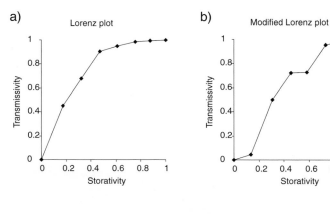

Figure B-4. (a) Lorenz plot and (b) modified Lorenz plot for porosity and permeability in well B (in a turbidite reservoir), using data from Table B-2.

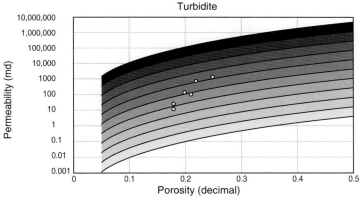

Figure B-5. Petrotype base map for well B, using porosity and permeability data from Table B-2.

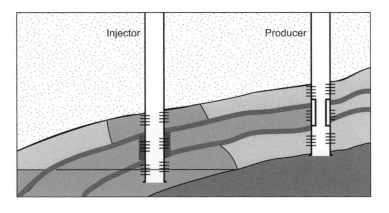

Figure B-6. In this case, shales between sand layers indicate that this is a commingled reservoir, and the layer with water breakthrough can be shut off effectively. After Arnold et al. (2004). Copyright © Schlumberger, Ltd. Used with permission.

Well C: A shallow-marine reservoir

The ordered Lorenz plot (Figure B-7a) shows significant heterogeneity. Average permeability is 288 md, and the CV is 2.15. However, the unordered stratigraphically modified LP (Figure B-7b) shows a similar profile. Six GHEs are in the reservoir (Figure B-8). Water is likely to enter the high-permeability upper layer and then to fall because of gravity. One should expect good sweep (Figure B-9) if vertical permeability is high enough.

Figure B-7. (a) Lorenz plot and (b) modified Lorenz plot for porosity and permeability data for well C (in a shallow-marine reservoir), using data from Table B-3.

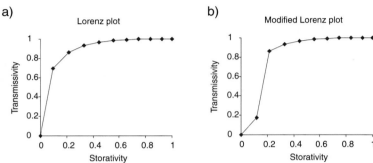

Figure B-8. Petrotype base map for well C, using porosity and permeability data from Table B-3.

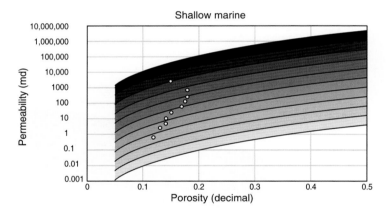

Figure B-9. Lorenz plot and modified Lorenz plot showing various sweep scenarios depending on the sorting of the layers. Shallow-marine reservoirs tend to be naturally sorted reservoirs — always coarsening upward — so they should have good sweep.

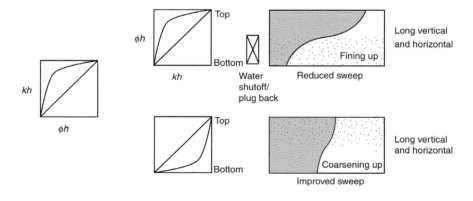

Summary

In each of the examples in this exercise, the modified and unmodified Lorenz plots give valuable insight into the vertical distribution of heterogeneities. That information, coupled with knowledge of lateral variability (from a geologic analogue), can be used to predict sweep patterns and likely recovery factors.

References

Ahmed, U., 2004, Making the most of maturing fields: Oilfield Review, **16**, no. 2, 1.

Amaefule, J. O., M. Altunbay, D. Tiab, D. G. Kersey, and D. K. Keelan, 1993, Enhanced reservoir description: Using core and log data to identify hydraulic (flow) units and predict permeability in uncored intervals/wells: SPE 26436.

Aminzadeh, F., 1996, "Geo-Engineer," the wave of the future: Journal of Petroleum Science and Engineering, **15**, no. 1, vii–x.

ASPO [Association for the Study of Peak Oil], 2002, http://www.peakoil.net/, accessed 13 July 2002.

Archer, J. S., and C. G. Wall, 1986, Petroleum engineering: Principles and practice: Graham and Trotman.

Arnold, R., D. B. Burnett, J. Elphick, T. J. Freeley III, M. Galbrun, M. Hightower, Z. Jiang, M. Khan, M. Lavery, F. Luffey, and P. Verbeek, 2004, Managing water — From waste to resource: Oilfield Review, **16**, no. 2, 26–41.

Bear, J., and Y. Bachmat, 1990, Introduction to modeling of transport phenomena in porous media: Kluwer Academic Publishers.

Brayshaw, A. C., R. Davies, and P. W. M. Corbett, 1996, Depositional controls on primary permeability and porosity at the bedform scale in fluvial reservoir sandstones, *in* P. A. Carling and M. Dawson, eds., Advances in fluvial dynamics and stratigraphy: John Wiley and Sons, 373–394.

Caers, J., 2005, Petroleum geostatistics: SPE.

Campbell, C., 2004, The end of the Oleocene: Geoscientist, **14**, no. 7, 18–19.

Coburn, T. C., J. M. Yarus, and R. L. Chambers, eds., 2006, Stochastic modeling and geostatistics: Principles, methods, and case studies, v. 2: AAPG Computer Applications in Geology No. 5, 23–33.

Corbett, P. W. M., 1992, Reservoir characterisation of a laminated sediment: Ph.D. thesis, Heriot-Watt University.

———, 1997, Geoengineers: A subject for debate: Petroleum Geoscience, **3**, 379.

———, 2002, Reservoir geonomics — Focussing on the essentials of reservoir geological modelling, special topic: Integration: First Break, **20**, no. 5, 299–301.

———, 2006, Petroleum geoengineering, the systematic measurement, interpretation and modeling of geological media for engineering the subsurface for the optimum exploitation of petroleum reservoirs: D.Sc. thesis, Heriot-Watt University.

Corbett, P. W. M., and J. L. Jensen, 1992a, Variation of reservoir statistics according to sample spacing and measurement type for some intervals in the Lower Brent Group: The Log Analyst, **33**, 22–41.

———, 1992b, Estimating the mean permeability: How many measurements do you need?: First Break, **10**, 89–94.

————, 1993a, Quantification of heterogeneity, a role for the minipermeameter in reservoir characterization, *in* C. P. North and D. J. Prosser, eds., Characterisation of fluvial and aeolian reservoirs: Geological Society [London] Special Publication 73, 433–442.

————, 1993b, An application of probe permeametry to the prediction of two-phase flow performance in laminated sandstones (lower Brent Group, North Sea): Marine and Petroleum Geology, **10**, no. 4, 335–346.

————, 2000, Lithological and zonal porosity-permeability distributions in the ARAB-D Reservoir, Utmaniyah field, Saudi Arabia: Discussion: AAPG Bulletin, **84**, 1365–1367.

Corbett, P. W. M., and D. Potter, 2004, Petrotyping: A basemap and atlas for navigating through permeability and porosity data for reservoir comparison and permeability prediction: Society of Core Analysts, SCA2004-30.

Corbett, P. W. M., S. Anggraeni, and D. Bowen, 1999, The use of the probe permeameter in carbonates — Addressing the problems of permeability support and stationarity: The Log Analyst, **40**, 316–326.

Corbett, P. W. M., D. Davies, and P. Gardiner, 2002, Addressing the challenges of teamwork and teamwork assessment in multidisciplinary education, special topic — Integration: First Break, **20**, no. 5, 302–304.

Corbett, P. W. M., Y. Ellabad, K. Egert, and S. Zheng, 2005, The geochoke test response in a catalogue of systematic geotype well test responses: SPE 93992.

Corbett, P. W. M., P. S. Ringrose, J. L. Jensen, and K. S. Sorbie, 1992, Laminated clastic reservoirs — The interplay of capillary pressure and sedimentary architecture: SPE 24699.

Corbett, P. W. M., S. Stromberg, P. Brenchley, and G. Geehan, 1994, Laminaset geometries in shallow marine sequences: Data from the Rannoch Formation (North Sea), Kennilworth [sic] Member (Utah) and Bencliff Grit (Dorset): Sedimentology, **41**, 729–745.

Cosentino, L., 2001, Integrated reservoir studies: Editions Technip.

Deffeyes, K. S., 2001, Hubbert's peak: The impending world oil shortage: Princeton University Press.

Dubrule, O., 2003, Geostatistics for seismic data integration in earth models: SEG Distinguished Instructor Series No. 6.

Eschard, R., and HERESIM Group, 1992, High-resolution sequence stratigraphy and reservoir characterization of a deltaic system from outcrop, cores and logs: IFP [Institut Français du Pétrole] Workshop.

Fookes, P., 1998, Integration of geology and engineering for site investigation: Quarterly Journal of Engineering Geology, **30**, part 4.

Frykman, P., 2002, The chalk reservoirs — How and where they differ from other reservoirs: 64th Annual Conference and Exhibition, EAGE, Abstract F-02.

Gunter, G. W., J. M. Finneran, D. J. Hartmann, and D. J. Miller, 1997, Early determination of reservoir flow units using an integrated petrophysical approach: SPE 38679, part 1, 373–380.

Harris, D. G., and C. H. Hewitt, 1977, Synergism in reservoir management — The geologic perspective: Journal of Petroleum Technology, **29**, no. 7, 761–770.

Heinburg, R., 2003, The party's over: Clairview Books.

Henson, R., A. C. Todd, and P. W. M. Corbett, 2002, Geologically based screening criteria for improved oil recovery projects: SPE 75148.

Holden, L., R. Hauge, O. Skare, and A. Skorstad, 1998, Modeling of fluvial reservoirs with object models: Mathematical Geology, **30**, 473–496.

Holditch, S. A., 2003, The increasing role of unconventional reservoirs in the future of the oil and gas business: Journal of Petroleum Technology, **55**, no. 11, 34–37, 79.

Jantschik, R., C. Strauss, and R. Weber, 1996, Sequence stratigraphy as a tool to improve reservoir management of the Eich/Koenigsgarten oil field (Upper Rhine Graben, Germany): SPE 36818.

Jensen, J. L., C. Glasbey, and P. W. M. Corbett, 1994, On the interaction of geology, measurement and statistical analysis of small scale permeability measurements: Terra Nova, **6**, 397–403.

Jensen, J. L., L. Lake, P. W. M. Corbett, and D. Goggin, 2000, Statistics for petroleum engineers and geoscientists, 2nd ed.: Elsevier.

Jones, A., J. Doyle, T. Jacobsen, and D. Konsvik, 1993, Which sub-seismic heterogeneities influence waterflood performance? A case study of a low net-to-gross fluvial reservoir, *in* H. J. De Haan, ed., New developments in improved oil recovery: Geological Society [London] Special Publication 84, 5–18.

Keith, D. W., 2001, Geoengineering: Nature, **409**, 420.

———, 2002, Geoengineering, *in* A. S. Goudie, ed., Encyclopedia of global change: Oxford University Press, 495–502.

Kirstetter, O., P. W. M. Corbett, J. Somerville, and C. MacBeth, 2006, Elasticity/saturation using flow simulation from an outcrop analogue for 4D seismic modelling: Petroleum Geoscience, **12**, 205–219.

Kjonsvik, D., J. Doyle, T. Jacobsen, and A. Jones, 1994, The effect of sedimentary heterogeneities on production from a shallow marine reservoir — What really matters?: SPE 28445.

Lake, L. W., 1989, Preface, *in* Reservoir characterization, v. 2: SPE Reprint Series No. 27, 3.

Larue, D. K., and Y. Yue, 2003, How stratigraphy influences oil recovery: A comparative reservoir database study concentrating on deepwater reservoirs: The Leading Edge, **22**, no. 4, 332–339.

Larter, S., A. C. Aplin, P. W. M. Corbett, N. Ementon, S. Chen, and S. Taylor, 1997, Reservoir geochemistry: A link between reservoir geology and engineering: SPE 28849.

Legrand, V., S. Zheng, and P. W. M. Corbett, 2007, Validation of geological models for reservoir simulation by modeling well test responses: Journal of Petroleum Geology, **30**, no. 1, 41–58.

Lord, A., P. Cooper, P. W. M. Corbett, N. Fuller, P. Rawson, and R. Rees, 1987, Microbiostratigraphy of the Volgian Stage, Volga River, U.S.S.R.: Neues Jahrbuch für Geologie und Palaeontologie, Monatsheft, 577–605.

MacBeth, C., 2007, An introduction to quantitative 4D seismic interpretation for dynamic reservoir description: EAGE Education Days, unpublished course notes.

Manzocchi, T., J. N. Carter, A. Skorstad, B. Fjellvoll, K. D. Stephen, J. A. Howell, J. D. Matthews, J. J. Walsh, M. Nepveu, C. Bos, J. Cole, P. Egberts, S. Flint, C. Hern, L. Holden, H. Hovland, H. Jackson, O. Kolbjørnsen, A. MacDonald, P. A. R. Nell, K. Onyeagoro, J. Strand, A. R. Syversveen, A. Tchistiakov, C. Yang, G. Yielding, and R. W. Zimmerman, 2008, Sensitivity of the impact of geological uncertainty on production from faulted and unfaulted shallow-marine oil reservoirs: Objectives and methods: Petroleum Geoscience, **14**, 3–14.

Marchetti, C., 1977, On geoengineering and the CO_2 problem: Climatic Change, **1**, no. 1, 59–68.

Meling, L. M., 2004, How and for how long is it possible to secure a sustainable growth in oil supply?: Presented at the Second WPC Regional Meeting, World Petroleum Council [WPC].

Mohammed, K., and P. W. M. Corbett, 2003, How many relative permeability samples do you need? A case study from a North African reservoir: Petrophysics, **44**, no. 4, 262–270.

Mohammed, K., P. W. M. Corbett, D. Bowen, A. W. Gardiner, and J. Buckman, 2002, Solution seams in the Mamuniyat Formation, El-Sharara-A field, SW Libya, impact on reservoir performance: Journal of Petroleum Geology, **25**, no. 3, 281–296.

Morton, K., S. Thomas, P. W. M. Corbett, and D. Davies, 2002, Detailed analysis of probe permeameter and vertical interference test permeability measurements in a heterogeneous reservoir: Petroleum Geoscience, **8**, 209–216.

Nordahl, K., 2004, A petrophysical evaluation of tidal heterolithic deposits: Application of a near wellbore model for reconciliation of scale dependent well data: Ph.D. thesis, Norwegian University of Science and Technology, Trondheim.

Nordahl, K., P. S. Ringrose, and R. Wen, 2005, Petrophysical characterization of a heterolithic tidal reservoir interval using a process-based modelling tool: Petroleum Geoscience, **11**, 17–28.

Olden, P., P. W. M. Corbett, R. Westerman, J. Somerville, N. Koustabeloulis, and B. G. D. Smart, 2001, Modeling combined fluid and stress change effects in the seismic response of a producing hydrocarbon reservoir: The Leading Edge, **20**, no. 10, 1154–1163.

Pickup, G., P. S. Ringrose, P. W. M. Corbett, K. S. Sorbie, and J. L. Jensen, 1995, Geology, geometry and effective flow: Petroleum Geoscience, **1**, no. 1, 37–42.

Pinisetti, M., 1999, Integrated numerical well test modeling in braided fluvial reservoirs: Ph.D. thesis, Heriot-Watt University.

Prasad, M., 2002, Acoustic measurements in unconsolidated sands at low effective pressure and overpressure detection: Geophysics, **67**, 405.

Rhoden, H. N., 1997, Chartered status: Geoscientist, **8.2**, 16.

Ringrose, P. S., and P. W. M. Corbett, 1994, Controls on two-phase fluid flow in heterogeneous sandstones, *in* J. Parnell, ed., Geofluids: Origin, migration and evolution of fluids in sedimentary basins: Geological Society [London] Special Publication 78, 141–150.

Ringrose, P. S., K. S. Sorbie, P. W. M. Corbett, and J. L. Jensen, 1993, Immiscible flow behaviour in laminated and cross-bedded sandstones: Journal of Petroleum Science and Engineering, **9**, 103–124.

Ringrose, P. S., K. Nordahl, and R. Wen, 2005, Vertical permeability estimation in heterolithic tidal deltaic sandstones: Petroleum Geoscience, **11**, 29–36.

Rowbotham, P. S., D. Marion, P. Lamy, E. Insalaco, P. A. Swaby, and Y. Bosseau, 2003, Multidisciplinary stochastic impedance inversion: Integrating geological understanding and capturing reservoir uncertainty: Petroleum Geoscience, **9**, 287–294.

Sagawa, A., P. W. M. Corbett, and D. Davies, 2000, Pressure transient analysis of reservoirs with a high permeability lens intersected by the well bore: Journal of Petroleum Science and Engineering, **27**, 165–177.

Shanley, K. W., and P. J. McCabe, 1994, Perspectives on the sequence of continental strata: AAPG Bulletin, **78**, 544–568.

Simmons, M. R., 2004, The peaking of oil: Reality or simply a myth?: Offshore Technology Conference, OTC 16860.

Smalley, C., W. Ross, C. E. Brown, T. P. Moulds, and M. J. Smith, 2007, Reservoir technical limits: A framework for maximising recovery from oil fields: SPE 109555.

Svrisky, D., A. Ryazanov, M. Pankov, P. W. M. Corbett, and A. Posysoev, 2004, Hydraulic flow units resolve reservoir description challenges in a Siberian oilfield: SPE 87056.

Thomas, S., P. W. M. Corbett, and J. L. Jensen, 1997, Permeability estimation within the Sherwood Sandstone, Morecambe Bay gas field: A numerical approach using probe permeametry, *in* C. D. Oakman, J. H. Martin, and P. W. M. Corbett, eds., Cores from the Northwest European Hydrocarbon Province: An illustration of geological applications from exploration to development: Geological Society [London], 197–203.

Toro-Rivera, M., P. W. M. Corbett, and G. Stewart, 1994, Well test interpretation in a heterogeneous braided fluvial reservoir: SPE 28828.

Tran, T., 1996, The missing scale and direct simulation of block effective properties: Journal of Hydrology, **183**, 37–56.

Tyler, N., and R. J. Finley, 1991, Architectural controls on the recovery of hydrocarbons from sandstone reservoirs, *in* A. D. Miall and N. Tyler, eds., The three-dimensional facies architecture of terrigenous clastic sediments and its implications for hydrocarbon discovery and recovery: SEPM Concepts in Sedimentology and Paleontology No. 3, 1–5.

Van Wagoner, J. C., C. R. Mitchum, K. M. Campion, and V. D. Rahmanian, 1990, Siliclastic sequence stratigraphy in well logs, cores, and outcrops: AAPG Methods in Exploration Series No. 7.

Weber, K., and L. C. van Geuns, 1990, Framework for constructing clastic reservoir simulation models: Journal of Petroleum Technology, **42**, 1248–1253, 1296–1297.

Wen, R.-J., A. W. Martinius, A. Naess, and P. S. Ringrose, 1998, Three-dimensional simulation of small-scale heterogeneity in tidal deposits — A process-based stochastic method, *in* A. Buccianti, G. Nardi, and A. Potenza, eds., Proceedings of the 4th Annual Conference of the International Association of Mathematical Geology, 129–134.

Worthington, P. F., 2005, Geoengineering studies: D.Eng. thesis, University of Birmingham.

Zheng, S.-Y., 1997, Well testing and characterisation of meandering fluvial channel reservoirs: Ph.D. thesis, Heriot-Watt University.

Zheng, S., P. W. M. Corbett, A. Ryseth, and G. Stewart, 2000, Uncertainty in well test and core permeability analysis: A case study in fluvial channel reservoir, northern North Sea, Norway: AAPG Bulletin, **84**, 1929–1954.

Index

A

accretionary channel bank, 48

acoustic impedance, 51, 52
    and porosity, 52
    distributions, 51
    facies dependency of, 52

acoustic properties, 20, 21
    laboratory measurement, 21

acoustic properties, and relative permeability, 54

acoustic properties, saturation, and stress, 32

acoustic response, prediction of, 37

acoustic-impedance distributions, 51

aggradation and curvature, interaction, 52

aggradation and progradation, interaction, 52

aggradation angle, 52

AI (*see* acoustic impedance)

Ainsa, Spain, 27, 29

air permeabilities, 58

alluvial fan, 27

Andrew oil field, North Sea, 3, 64

Angola, 29

anisotropy, and sweep efficiency, 50

anisotropy, permeability, 32, 78

architectural matrices, 11

architectural matrix, 41

architecture of rocks, 25–27
    and intrareservoir seals, 25
    and optimized recovery, 27
    and reservoir flow units, 25
    progradational parasequence, 25

arithmetic mean, 28, 29, 31, 35, 38, 46, 73, 74, 76–77, 78
    estimation of, 76–77

Asian Institute of Technology, Thailand, 10

aspect ratio, 29, 62

of sandstone bodies relative to well spacing, 62

aspect ratio histogram, 75

Association for the Study of Peak Oil and Gas, 63

atolls, 2, 64

attribute analysis, 4

Auk oil field, North Sea, 3, 64

Australia, 10

B

back barrier, 2, 27, 64

barrier bars, 2, 64

barrier island, 27

beach/stacked tidal sandstone, 35

bedset, 23, 33, 46, 47, 48, 70
    scale, 33, 46
        as "missing scale," 46

bedset geopseudos, 46

bedset-scale heterogeneity, 43

Bencliff Grit, 28

bio/sequence stratigraphy, 30

Blaze Canyon, Book Cliffs, Utah, 53

Book Cliffs, Utah, 53

Book Cliffs model, simulation, 53–55
    impedance contrasts, after water injection, 55
    pressure depletion, 55

BP, 64

Brae oil field, North Sea, 3, 64

braid plain, 27

braided fluvial reservoirs, 59, 73, 79
    and double-matrix porosity, 59

braided fluvial setting, 32

braided river, 27

braided system, heterogeneity of, 34, 39
    pixel model, 39

braided systems, 75

Brazil, 10, 29
Brent Group, North Sea, 32
bypassed oil, 41

C

capillary forces, 43
capillary pressure, 16–17, 45, 49
    and pore-size distributions, 16
    and rock typing, 16
capillary-pressure curve, 16–17, 18
    shape of, and texture of sediment, 17
carbonate platforms, 2, 64
carbonate ramps, 2, 64
carbonates, 2, 35, 64
    platform-margin, 2, 64
    platforms, 2
    ramps, 64
    restricted-platform, 2, 64
cardinal sine variogram, 38
cement, distribution of, 50
central limit theorem, 14
chalk, 18, 23
channel abandonments, 33
channel-fill sandstone, 35
clay drapes, 33
coastal-plain system, 39
    object model, 39
coefficient of variation (CV), 33, 34, 35, 59,
        65, 74, 76, 77, 78, 79, 81
collated cokriging, 52
commingled layers, 62
commingled-flow reservoirs, 71, 81
compaction, reservoir, 56
compartmentalized oil, 67
compartments, 41
composite sand body, 79
composite systems, 75
compressional velocity and permeability,
        21
core plug, 14, 15, 18
core skills, petroleum geoengineer, 24–36
core-plug, cell, 15
core-plug data, 33, 35, 56, 78, 79
    and heterogeneity at bed scale, 56
    compared with probe measurements,
        35

correlation, spatial, 36
CO_2, 9, 20
    removal from atmosphere, 9
    sequestration, 9, 10
Crawford field, North Sea, 3, 64
Cretaceous sandstone, 18
crevasse-splay sandstone, 35
cross flow, 62, 65, 66, 79
cross-flow reservoirs, 65, 71
cross-scaling, 58, 69
    as distinguished from upscaling, 69
cubic variogram, 37, 38
curvature and progradation, interaction, 52
CV (*see* coefficient of variation)

D

Dan field, 16
Darcy's law, 13, 15, 22, 23
databases, 62
    and permeability, 62
debris flow, 3
debris-flow reservoir, 64
decline rates, oil production, 63
deepwater reservoirs, 62
deltas, 2, 64
    fan deltas, 2
    fluvial/wave-modified, 2, 64
    fluvially dominated, 2, 64
    strandplain/wave-dominated, 2, 64
    wave-dominated, 2, 64
Denmark, 16
depositional architecture, 39–40
    and geologic models, 39–40
depositional environments, classified, 27
depositional models, 4
depositional systems, 2
    and unrecovered mobile oil, 2
diagenesis, 26
diagenetic mapping, 4
digital petrophysics, 43
dip, 49
directional permeability, 29
discrete-fault population, 49
distal channel, 35
distal delta front, 27
distal delta lobe, 48